TRAUMA

WITHDRAWN

This Book
was Donated To

LRC Stoke Park

Date: 22/11/05

For a complete list of Management Books 2000 titles, visit our web-site on http://www.mb2000.com

THE LIBRARY
GUILDFORD COLLEGE
of Further and Higher Education

TRAUMA

How to recognise the symptoms and help the victims

Eva Roman
and Roger le Duc-Barnett

616.8521 ROM

145719

Copyright © Eva Roman and Roger le Duc-Barnett 2000

All rights reserved. No part of this publication may be reproduced, stored in a retrieval system, or transmitted in any form or by any means, electronic, mechanical, photocopying, recording, or otherwise without the prior permission of the publishers.

First published in 2000 by Management Books 2000 Ltd
Cowcombe House
Cowcombe Hill
Chalford
Gloucestershire GL6 8HP
Tel. 01285 760 722
Fax. 01285 760 708
E-mail: mb2000@compuserve.com

Printed and bound in Great Britain by Biddles, Guildford

This book is sold subject to the condition that it shall not, by way of trade or otherwise, be lent, resold, hired out, or otherwise circulated without the publisher's prior consent in any form of binding or cover other than that in which it is published and without a similar condition including this condition being imposed upon the subsequent purchaser.

British Library Cataloguing in Publication Data is available
ISBN 1-85252-365-5

Contents

TRAUMA
Dealing With Post-Traumatic Stress

INTRODUCTION

From the moment of birth to the individual's final demise, life is a journey which leads human beings through a series of life spans. Each stage provides opportunities for development, both physical and psychological.

Stress is part of the human condition, as common as taking breath and food. In fact, we depend upon and actually create for ourselves a daily background of nagging stress to jostle us into getting a hundred things done which by choice alone we might not otherwise bother with. This kind of self-induced stress is owner-friendly – we were taught how to produce it in childhood by parents and children alike. It was introduced in various guises, as 'self-discipline' for example, and has remained ever since as the persistent inner voice demanding that 'unless you get on with this or that right now, there will be trouble'. A harsh taskmaster, expert in dishing out guilt.

Serious externally generated stress, particularly long-term, is another matter. It can eventually threaten health of mind, body and mood. Disabling energy-sapping frustration can build on growing tension in important events, in business or personal circumstances, making exceptional demands on someone who may not be able to cope successfully or in good time.

Tolerance levels for resisting pressure, like most things, vary from person to person but there is very little subjective or anecdotal evidence to support the claim that some people actually 'thrive' on stress.

The signs and symptoms arising in response to intolerable stress, possibly caused through a traumatic incident, are many. In today's society, it is used in a destructive way. The usual image of the 'stressed' individual is someone who is not coping, who is making inappropriate decisions, is tearful or aggressive, showing signs of withdrawing from friends and family or who could be eating, drinking or smoking more than usual.

Anywhere along the way and at any time, people can be involved, either directly or indirectly in a traumatic event. The word ***trauma*** derives from the Greek – a piercing of the skin. Such piercing will cause damage to the tissues and produce wounds.

Dr Sigmund Freud used the word metaphorically to emphasise how the mind too can be pierced and wounded by traumatic events (*Beyond the Pleasure Principle*, Freud S., 1920). When trauma strikes, it ruptures the person's sense of natural continuity and results in a break in that individual's life-story line, which then requires treatment which will help to mend broken bridges in order to encourage healing.

Post Traumatic Stress is the result of experiencing or even observing a disturbing or traumatic event outside the range of normal human experience – anything from a minor incident to a major disaster. For example:

- accidents (minor or severe)
- assault
- violent bereavement
- disasters
- crime

This is likely to affect the person's normal behaviour and relationships with family, friends and colleagues.

At work, this could lead to a serious deterioration of the individual's output, lack of concentration and increased absenteeism. Also noticeable might be, as previously mentioned, an increased use of both prescribed drugs and alcohol or tobacco.

Although what follows in this book concentrates largely on industry, commerce and the public sector, one must be aware that trauma takes place anywhere within society as a whole. Whether it is an incident in the workplace, at home or on a journey to and from work, the reactions will be the same. It affects the survivor or bystander, the family, the community and the workplace. People have to live with trauma's direct effect upon their lives as well as the indirect consequences, namely upon society in general.

The following chapters are intended to give the reader an awareness of what trauma is, its effect on the individual and how the ripples of the trauma affect the workplace and society. Trauma can range from the loss of a digit to rape, mugging or falling down the stairs at home. Another group of traumas which enters into all our lives comes through the media which covers the national disasters such as train or air crashes, earthquakes, war and so on.

The book will examine the way trauma strikes, its effect on the individual and how an impact is made on the immediate surrounding community, both inside and outside the workplace. It will explain how the process of psychological debriefing and supportive counselling can help to relieve some of the pain and suffering and work towards a positive outcome in the lives of those affected.

The book is not intended as a do-it-yourself guide to trauma. It requires years of study and experience to help traumatised individuals back on the road to recovery. The aim is to make the reader aware of (a) the consequences that might arise through lack of understanding and (b) the need to provide early intervention so that the individual is prevented from slipping into the more serious, debilitating and long-term condition of Post Traumatic Stress Disorder.

1

Crisis Intervention

Whenever a critical incident occurs to either an individual or a group of people, it can cause psychological trauma. Any abnormal, violent event which goes beyond the coping mechanism of the individual to whom it is happening can produce shock to the system.

Shock in itself is not an illness. It is a condition which either occurs as a result of an accident, injury, blood or fluid loss, heart attack or an allergy caused by certain medication or food, or the sight of something very unpleasant happening to someone else such as a physical attack.

Not everyone is affected – the outcome of the occurrence depends very much on personality and 'type'. Why are some people affected by traumatic experiences and others walk away seemingly unaffected?

What is it that pushes some of us into chaos and confusion, while others manage to shake off any unpleasant after-effects? Psychologists may draw attention to biological reasons and social scientists may suggest a mixture of both biology and nurture! It is possible that both experience and biology have a relevant interplay at the interface to the introduction of traumatic experience.

However, we often communicate fear and we do this through the production of certain chemicals which either cause us to face what is happening or flee. This syndrome is called 'Fright, Fight, Flight or Freeze' and the chemical is adrenaline, produced by the suprarenal glands or adrenal glands, found on the upper pole of each kidney. Stimulation of these glands produce adrenaline which provides a boost of energy to the parts of the body most in need of it. Another way to experience fear is through the sense of smell. We are therefore constantly communicating something through our behaviour or our secretion of perspiration and body fluids.

Crisis Intervention

Crisis intervention to a traumatic incident is not counselling but a type of 'psychological First Aid' which is offering both practical support – for example, transport or clothing – and seeing to personal comfort, relaying information and communicating with the incident authorities and so on.

Psychological support

Psychological support is 'containing' and 'holding' the distressed. This is offering enough psychological support to keep the traumatised in a 'state of comfort' and personal safety – in a sense, taking control for them, giving them space and the opportunity to vent their feelings and emotions without contradictions or judgement.

This phase can last for approximately the first twenty-four to forty-eight hours, according to the severity of the incident. For example, in a national disaster, this can be more protracted, sometimes for two to three days, but in a localised incident this can be significantly shorter, lasting for only a matter of hours.

However, before the next stage of the healing process begins, which concerns itself with Post Traumatic Stress Reduction (Debriefing), the brain needs to be given a chance to process what has gone on, which is why debriefing should not be attempted before forty-eight to seventy-two hours after an incident, sometimes even longer. It is certainly not advisable to start a counselling relationship or assessment for counselling until approximately two to four weeks after the incident since the brain is unable to commence looking at some of the big philosophical questions that are essential for the survivor to reflect on and make sense of.

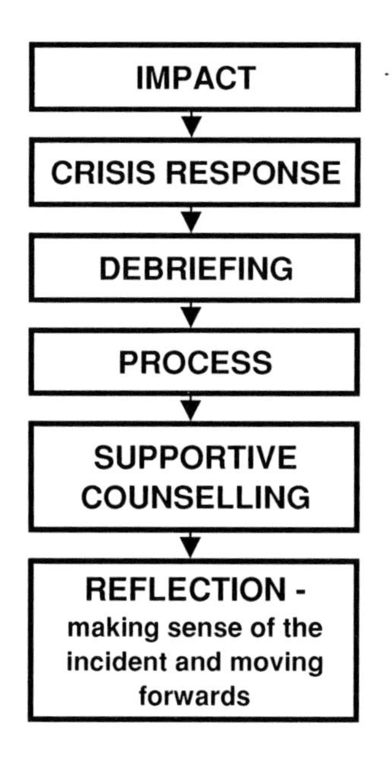

Fig 1: Stages of support and natural body coping mechanism

After an injury or traumatic incident has taken place, adrenaline is released from the adrenal glands. Messages from the brain pass instructions that an increase of adrenaline be directed via the blood stream to specific parts of the body in order to protect or strengthen the injured part.

Someone who has sustained a fracture often feels little or no pain since the adrenal response prepares the individual for 'fright – flight – fight or freeze'. For example, should it become necessary to flee from something threatening, a boost of adrenaline would be required by the legs. Naturally, as the adrenaline response wears off, pain will increase.

The following illustration is to stress the importance of a knowledge of how these powerful chemicals surge through the body on excitement or shock. If looked at carefully, one can understand with clarity people's natural responses to trauma.

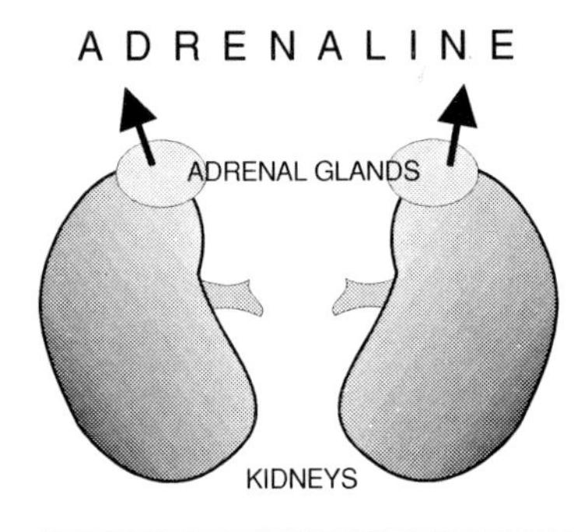

Adrenaline - is secreted by the adrenal glands

Location - at the apex of the kidneys

Function - produces effects similar to the stimulation of the sympathetic nervous system, generally preparing the body for 'fright, flight or fight'.

Notes:

The ***adrenal*** or ***supradrenal glands*** lie on the upper pole of each kidney. The adrenal glands consist of an outer, yellowish part, the cortex, which produces ***cortisol*** (hydrocortisone), a close relation of cortisone, and an upper medullary portion producing both ***adrenaline*** (epinephrine) and ***noradrenaline*** (norepinephrine).

These substances are secreted under the control of the sympathetic nervous system. The secretion is increased in conditions of emotion such as anger and fear, and in states of asphyxia and starvation. An increase raises the blood pressure in order to combat the shock produced by these emergencies.

Noradrenaline raises the blood pressure by stimulating the muscular fibres in the walls of the blood vessels, causing them to contract. ***Adrenaline*** aids carbohydrate metabolism by increasing the output of glucose from the liver.

The important hormones secreted by the adrenal cortex are ***hydrocortisone***, ***aldosterone*** and ***corticosterone***, which are intimately concerned with metabolism, growth, renal function and muscle tone. These functions are essential to life.

(16th Edition, 'Anatomy and Physiology for Nurses' Evelyn Price)

Figure 2: Adrenaline.

The above refers to shock caused by physical injuries where parts of the body will require medical attention. Another condition is that of shock without actual physical injury but with psychosomatic symptoms (paralysis) which can occur if someone suddenly hears very bad news or has just witnessed a relative, friend or colleague at work being involved in an accident. Any other number of reasons could include physical abuse where there was no actual personal involvement. Shock can very quickly develop, particularly if it causes intense worry which will assist in worsening the condition. This idea will be developed later in this chapter.

A ***crisis*** is the moment or time of severe danger or trouble. This manifests when an individual is completely involved in the incident, i.e. the rescue of casualties from a disaster, where a person may also have been in personal danger or risk to him- or herself. Another example shows people being involved in a hold-up and, although they may not be personally injured, they will experience extreme fear for their lives. Several thoughts will occur to the person immediately after the incident. These are:

- What has or is happening to me?
- What is going to become of me?
- What if I don't get better?
- Am I safe?

This is the time when a qualified, empathetic carer should be on hand to give practical support and assistance to the people who most need human contact at a time of severe crisis, particularly reassuring the survivor that he or she is safe in the carer's hands.

PSYCHOLOGICAL REACTIONS TO A TRAUMATIC INCIDENT

What people will feel:

FEAR:	of damage to self and others of being left alone of breaking down
HELPLESSNESS:	what can one do in the face of such tragedy?
GRIEF:	for death, injury or loss
ANGER:	at what has happened and why it has happened
GUILT:	for being alive; for surviving, for not being hurt
SHAME:	for seeming helpless and emotional
HOPE:	for the future

The person or people who are performing the task of crisis intervention will only be involved with the injured and/or traumatised individual for a relatively short period and will basically work in an emergency capacity in order to help the survivor cope with the immediate aftermath.

Crisis intervention is a one-off procedure which is offered to survivors immediately following an incident. At this stage, any traumatised person will be unable to look unemotionally at any logical or urgent requirements. The carer's job becomes that of a 'prop' for the traumatised person, giving support and any relevant information which may be essential immediately after the incident.

During crisis intervention, the carer rarely gives any psychological advice since the survivors are too overwhelmed by the incident to react to counselling and, at this stage, need personal space to measure their own coping mechanism. What the survivors look for is support, reassurance and relevant information to assist with their most pressing needs.

It could well be that the most pressing needs are in the nature of First Aid if ***shock signs and symptoms*** are apparent.

Signs of shock

1. The person's face will be very pale, often grey. The skin will feel clammy or may sweat, often profusely, but will feel cold to the touch. This is an indication that all is not well since someone with clammy skin should feel hot, yet the skin feels cold. At the same time, anyone feeling hot would have a flushed appearance, but anyone in shock appears pale.

2. The person's breathing will be fairly rapid but shallow: this is often called 'puppy-dog yapping'. Because breathing is shallow, due to possible blood loss, less oxygen is inhaled. There may also be a gasping for breath called 'air hunger'.

3. The third sign is a fast but thready pulse. When first taken it may be quite regular, but as time goes by, it may become more rapid, weak and irregular.

Symptoms of shock

There are many symptoms that can be displayed by anyone in shock and trauma. Not everyone will have precisely the same ones and they will also depend on the severity and degree of the condition. The following main symptoms are often found.

- Since blood is pumped to the injured parts by redistribution, it will be withheld from other vital organs such as the brain, heart, stomach and so on. The person may feel nauseous, particularly if a heavy meal has recently been consumed. Vomiting may actually take place.

- A person in shock is often extremely thirsty, at times pathetically so, particularly if blood or fluid loss has occurred.

- Restlessness is another feature, where the person is unable to remain still for long. This could pose problems, particularly when a fracture has been sustained.

- It would be inadvisable to put too much trust into information given by the person since confusion related to the incident may be experienced. If this is combined with restlessness, the person should not be left alone.

- Anxiety is another common symptom. Many things will prey on such people's minds, particularly if they have important meetings to attend, deadlines to honour or any number of other reasons.

- Nervousness and suspicion can feature in shock. The person could show mistrust and challenge anything being done to help. He or she may well become uncooperative, argumentative or downright aggressive.

- Someone in shock may start to shiver and complain of feeling cold. This may be due to internal bleeding or heavy fluid loss such as vomiting.

Denial is sometimes found in someone who either refuses or is unable to come to terms with the fact that 'something nasty' has just occurred. However long they deny the incident, eventually they do come to terms with their plight and admit that all is not well. Reassurance is most important in such situations, particularly taking charge of decisions on behalf of the survivor.

TREATMENT FOR SHOCK

- ☑ Concentrate on REASSURANCE to alleviate further anxiety.
- ☑ If the survivor's face is pale, raise the legs above the heart level.
- ☑ Keep the survivor warm by wrapping blankets round (over and under).
- ☑ Provided the survivor is not injured, a warm cup of sweet tea can be given - to be sipped at intervals.
- ☑ Where there is no improvement - this could be due to internal injuries - and the person gets worse, remove him or her to hospital.

2

Tools for Crisis Intervention

It is a well known fact that whenever a critical incident occurs where people are hurt or where they have been bystanders at the scene, someone comes forward with very good intentions but little knowledge of the correct procedures to employ.

As mentioned in the last chapter, someone who is in shock can be given sips of sweetened tea at intervals but only if there are no physical injuries – this assessment requires knowledge of First Aid so that a preliminary examination can be given. Lack of skills can often do more harm than good and all the good will in the world will only cause further problems.

There appears to be a morbid fascination which glues people to the ground in order not to miss observing all the gory details. This achieves the very opposite of what is needed, with people getting underfoot and preventing trained carers from getting on with the real assistance to those who urgently require it.

It must be said that not everyone is suitable or possesses the right characteristics to carry out crisis intervention. It may well be possible that a critical incident re-awakes some distant memory, long since buried in the unconscious mind which then causes reactions in the very person who is attempting to help. Others may have an aversion to the sight of severe bleeding; they would be better off away from such scenes. Squeamishness has no place in situations which contain blood and gore.

Carers need to have a practical approach to crisis situations and be prepared to roll up their sleeves and get stuck in.

Since the traumatised individuals will have developed reactions which to them seem abnormal, the carer should possess healthy caring skills. There is a very real need to be accepted by the survivor and to develop a fast rapport. Any feelings of antipathy for whatever reason will interfere with the ability of the carer to take control of the situation and deal authoritatively with any immediate problems of concern to the survivor. Good communication skills are therefore essential adjuncts since the person might be in shock and will find it difficult to understand and give information which may be important towards carrying out immediate support.

Once all practicalities have been dealt with, it is advisable to remain with the person who might otherwise lose all the benefit and support already given. However, when more professional help arrives, the carer must be prepared to relinquish control and leave the next stage to other staff.

Carers need to remember that unless they look after their own needs and take care of themselves, they may end up having adverse reactions which in turn will require help from other sources.

Adrenaline can sometimes distort our image and sense of ourselves and it is important that we allow our manager or supervisor to be responsible for telling us that enough is enough.

Adrenaline is a stimulant and therefore fires us up which makes it difficult for us to be aware of our fallibility. We therefore need to rely on good strong management for our own health's sake.

It would hardly help if carers became so hyped up that they ended up by appearing more nervous than the survivor who has just gone through a traumatic incident.

- An ***exchange of names*** (usually first names) will help identify people to each other although sometimes where there is evidence of shock, the person may not even remember who he or she is. One or two simple questions often help establish initial information, after which, listening to anything which might throw some further light on the situation will be more helpful than to fire lots of questions at the survivor, most of which will not even register.

- ***Good listening skills*** also help to establish trust which needs to be built up fast so that survivors feel that here is someone who knows what he or she is doing and will have their best interest at heart.
- If carers appear ***confident***, show that they understand the problem and will deal with it to the best of their ability, the topsy-turvy world in which the survivor finds him- or herself will appear less frightening.
- ***Perception*** on the part of the carer also goes a long way and often helps to speed up ways of providing fast intervention.
- As was mentioned earlier, ***effective communication skills*** are a necessary adjunct to the qualities required as a carer, particularly in situations where others may try to make decisions on behalf of the survivors which are not in their best interests. The carer must then intervene on the person's behalf and make certain that the reasons for the possible objections are really valid.
- It may also be necessary to ***pass on accurate information*** to officials also involved in rescue operations and if the carer is less than articulate, it may show a confusing and inaccurate picture. A carer, well conversant with proper procedures will be able to portray trust in his or her ability to see what needs to be done, will appreciate in what order of priority it requires attention and will apply common sense to create order out of chaos.
- ***Embarrassment has no place*** within crisis situations where people may involuntarily lose control of their bodily functions, possibly soil themselves by vomiting or in other ways. Any adverse reaction shown by an untrained carer can cause more embarrassment on the part of the survivor and spoil any carefully established rapport.
- Any practical issues requiring immediate attention need to be carried out with the ***least amount of fuss***, thereby avoiding further upset and anxiety for the already traumatised person.

Main skills required in crisis intervention

1. Befriending skills **2. Listening skills**

3. Communication skills **4. Practical skills**

1. Befriending skills

Approachability

Authority

Prepared to establish an autocratic relationship (take control)

Listening

Empathy (not being embarrassed by emotions)

Being a practical person (prepared to roll sleeves up and get stuck in)

Not being squeamish

Good communication skills

Able to give control back

Able to take care of oneself

Being comfortable with oneself (no recent bereavement, no unresolved trauma)

2. Listening skills

Being able to build trust quickly

Confidence

Having an air of authority and understanding

Perceptiveness

3. Communication skills

Ability to champion cause

Ability to relate accurate story

Ability to instil trust

4. Practical skills

Common sense

Seeing what needs to be done

Not being embarrassed to use authority

3

Purpose of Post Traumatic Stress Reduction (Debriefing) – The Structured Approach

A managerial debriefing within the workplace or elsewhere in the community will usually take place after a specific incident to see if the job has been done in a satisfactory way. It will require checking to make sure if it could have been done in a better way and, with hindsight, to see if there were any other issues around that were omitted at the planning stage that could have been overcome in a better, more productive way.

Psychological debriefing is slightly different in that it is a way of working to help the client/group see what actually happened in the mind at the impact of the trauma. It is a process which enables the client/group to be aware of the overall story and for them to see themselves within the whole. It is a structured intervention which once begun needs to follow through the various phases of the model to enable the story to unfold. Its purpose is for nothing more than being able to see the whole story and in the telling and recalling to be able to make sense of the incident in some way and, for some to receive catharsis. There is nothing magical or mystical about the process, for it leads one from the point of normality – everyday routine, to the point of impact and then trauma, through the thoughts, emotions and normality of the experiences of normal body coping mechanisms to a conclusion.

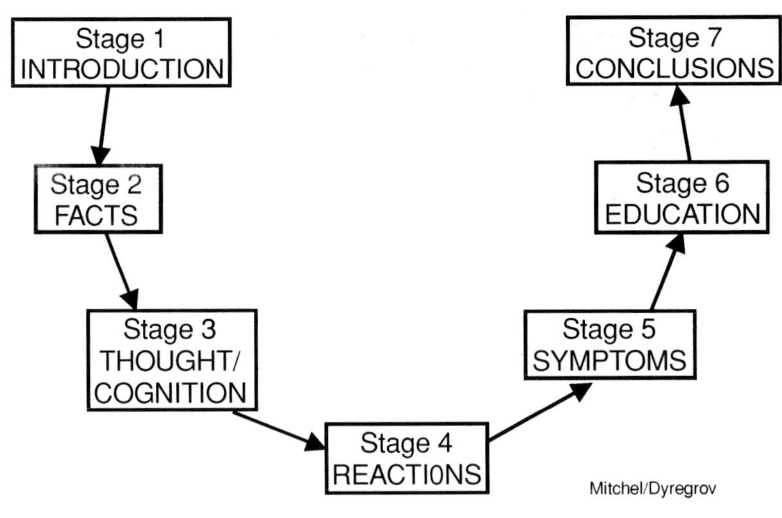

Fig 3: Debriefing

This process is very important. The stages lead from a beginning to a content and an exploration of thoughts and feelings. This is an opportunity for the debriefer to offer some teaching and become aware of the normality of the feelings experienced to a period of possible resolution and disengagement, this being the conclusion.

There is much controversy around about the whole area of debriefing and counselling as we mentioned in the opening pages of this book. However, as clinicians with many hours of experience, we strongly believe in the value of the process of psychological debriefing.

It appears that where there is an element of team spirit within the group, where people work together and know one another, then the process appears to be more beneficial than when one brings together a group of people unknown to each other.

The idea of debriefing is really quite simple. The brain is jolted through the trauma and from holding on to a painful image or piece of information. Because of the focus of this image, the brain has difficulty in releasing it. The survivor goes over and over the incident in his or her mind, causing more hurt and pain as images occur of what may have been done, could have done, or not done and so on. Thoughts begin to race and the survivor becomes overwhelmed by the reaction to the trauma. Time is needed to process it, but usually the brain cannot let the trauma go.

Debriefing takes that piece of information from the forefront of our minds and helps us to process it, to store it in the base of the brain known as the amygdala.

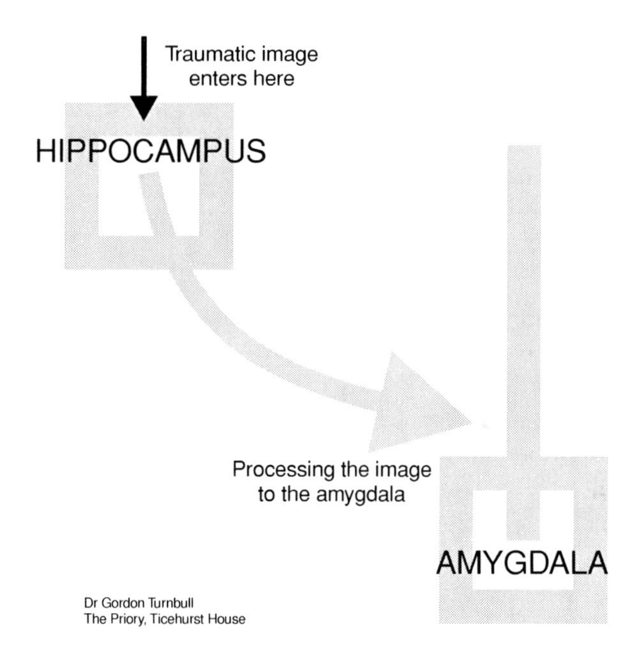

Figure 4: Helping process intrusive thoughts

Although this process appears simple, it must be noted that the debriefer has had many hours of training, before coming to the point of actually doing a debrief. The lead debriefer should always be backed up by a skilled colleague who is there for support, observation and who is able to take over if the process continues for some considerable time.

Sometimes, however, developments point to the possibility that the period of debriefing should be curtailed since it may induce overwhelming thoughts and feelings if the process is not handled correctly.

Not only is the immediate recipient involved but members of his or her family may be affected and others like friends or work colleagues will also bear the brunt. The survivor who was originally involved or saw what happened may not be willing to share the experience with anyone and will cling to the unpleasant after-effects stoically hoping that by being 'strong', things will eventually return to normal.

Some people eventually learn to live with the memories of the incident but the in-between period tends to be excruciatingly painful, anxiety ridden and totally out of context in comparison to their every-day coping mechanism. Meanwhile, they may lose working hours through the inability to find the energy to even get to their place of work, let alone cope with the daily pressures.

In the case of a multiple incident where several people were involved in the same event, a group debriefing is usually advisable. This gives all participants the chance to share in the re-experiencing of the incident and to enable them to put their impressions into proper perspective thereby making sense of jumbled thoughts. People often see the incident in their mind's eye in a certain way and are positively convinced that this is the way it happened. By sharing with others who were involved in the same incident, the picture may change and reality is finally achieved.

Since the debriefing process is a totally structured set of stages through which all those attending are led, everyone has the opportunity to re-relate the incident according to his or her own belief.

In this particular model, shown as Figure 3, there are seven stages which are explored and discussed (there are a number of other models). No-one is forced to join in. Some people find it very painful to re-live such experiences but it is usually found that once people start to take part, most others will follow.

① Introduction

The ***introduction*** will be used to explain what will take place and what is expected of everyone. No pressure is used, no blame attached to anyone and it is made clear that the session will not be used as a means for complaints by any member of the group.

② The facts

Stage two concerns itself with details of what happened and where everyone was at the time.

③ Thoughts and cognition

The group discuss what thoughts ran through their minds at the time of the incident, both immediately after and some time later. Again this helps to put everything into perspective.

④ Reactions

Stage four is probably the most difficult for participants. This concerns itself with people's reactions and emotions during and after the incident. Most people find this very painful since it is a re-living and re-experiencing of the emotions felt at the time of the incident.

⑤ Symptoms

The fifth stage looks at the symptoms which the participants of the group may be experiencing. These could range from mild depression and the inability to forget what has happened to shock and difficulty accepting what has happened. Survivors may suffer from lack of sleep where thoughts and pictures of the incident prevent them from dropping off to sleep. Alternatively, dreams and nightmares take over which again stops continuous sleep as this is interrupted by wakeful periods due to the nightmares. Concentration also suffers and the memory plays tricks, stopping people from retaining important information. Some individuals get very anxious about the future and what might become of them.

Anger symptoms become very real and this can be directed at anyone or at any situation. This in turn can change to guilt, not only because the anger was misplaced but the person may realise this and consequently feel guilty and inadequate. There may even be a sense of failure due to the individual's inability to take control of his or her life, which can produce social isolation.

One of the more common symptoms refers to fear that the incident might be repeated and that personal safety is still at risk. Life tends to become very unreal and people often see no way out, which can produce even more unwelcome symptoms. The ability to share these symptoms with colleagues, friends and others can be of very real benefit and produce relief that one is not alone.

⑥ Education

During the sixth stage, the group goes through an educational input during which those thoughts, reactions, symptoms and feelings are examined and explained. Questions are put to everyone about what has taken place during the meeting and what the outcome may be to each individual.

During this session, normalisation will be explained. Although everyone has been through an abnormal situation, their reactions, whatever they were and however distressing, are 'NORMAL'.

⑦ Conclusion

The last stage concerns itself with the conclusion of the debriefing. Survivors will be encouraged to look to the future and try to create an action plan, for example, how they will conduct themselves during the next days and weeks, whether there are any main areas which are of particular concern and what support and assistance they may need. Should this become necessary, it is important to advise anyone where this support might be obtained. Survivors will require alternatives so that they can have a choice for further help.

Some groups may decide to have a further meeting in a few weeks, others may wish to try coping on their own. There may be one or two survivors who would prefer to see a counsellor on a one-to-one basis for a few sessions. All of these choices should be made available.

Lastly, the debriefer/s should make him/her/themselves available for a while, after the debriefing, to give people a chance to have a quiet private word or two after the session before the meeting is terminated.

4

Preparation for Debriefing

A look behind the scenes

As was previously mentioned, post traumatic stress can happen as a result of experiencing or even observing a 'disturbing or traumatic event outside the range of normal human experience' (DSM-IV – the American Diagnostic and Statistical Manual - see Appendix I). This can be anything from a minor incident to a major disaster. The incident is therefore caused by an abnormal episode beyond the normal coping mechanism of the individual.

Before any psychological debriefing can take place, arrangements for either groups or one-to-one interventions will have to be carried out. These preparations will enable a comfortable foundation for a framework to be achieved.

After an appropriate time lapse between ***crisis intervention*** and the start of ***debriefing*** (ideally seventy-two hours to two weeks) a group or one-to-one psychological debriefing should be organised. This requires strict adherence to the many facets which are required for the smooth running of the session.

Only those directly involved in the incident should receive crisis intervention, followed at a later stage by psychological debriefing. Those who were not immediately involved should not be allowed to join the session except by prior agreement with the group. However, a second group could be set up to deal with any adverse reactions which might occur if it was felt necessary.

It is advisable that no more than ten people (excluding the

debriefer/s) should be present. It is the function of the lead debriefer and colleague to establish and maintain the structure of the session and to see that the stages of psychological debriefing are visited and dealt with in an appropriate and professional manner. As explained in the last chapter, the second debriefer is there to assist in any way which may be helpful to the group.

If at all possible, discussions involving the planning of the debriefing should take place between management and co-ordinator. At this stage, it will be decided who is to attend the psychological debriefing, what is required to achieve the most beneficial way forward and the material things required to provide basic necessities for the group debrief, e.g. white board and so on.

It is important at this stage to realise that the session may continue over lunch or tea break and therefore adequate preparation should be made for refreshments. The time needed for a psychological debriefing session can be anything from one to four hours. To help with the management of this process, a checklist will be found at the end of this chapter.

It should be understood that other authorities such as the Police, Health and Safety Executive and possibly the Personnel or Human Resources Department will require statements should an industrial accident have taken place. These statements in no way interfere with the debriefing process which is designed to provide maximum positive support to every member of the group or to the individual.

The psychological debriefing should seek to enable the group or individual to leave with a positive approach to the future. To that end, the group or individual will need to be given options on how to proceed should they find it necessary to seek further help.

Both debriefers should make themselves available for any worries that individuals may have regarding future support which may be required.

The above points relate mainly to management, staff and employees in industry. However, trauma can effect anybody anywhere at any time. It is quite possible that reactions normally experienced will begin to appear which, despite all effort on the part of the individual to erase, will persist. Help is therefore required in order to obtain the right kind of support by qualified personnel.

Naturally it will be of benefit to share these reactions with family, close friends and anyone else who has been involved in the same incident. This often helps, but should these reactions persist, it would be advisable to seek the assistance of a GP, counsellors, or other like-minded agencies who are trained and qualified in trauma.

Procedures for Management before a psychological debriefing:

- A conversation with Management/Personnel/Human Resources and so on, is required in order to establish that a psychological debriefing will be required by staff.
- It is necessary that the debriefing staff are informed of details of the incident and how many people were directly or indirectly involved. It is also advisable to mention any physical injuries or deaths.
- It must be understood that a psychological debriefing session deals with aspects of the incident. Grievances about management problems which might arise and which are non-related to the incident should be dealt with separately.
- It is advisable that the same debriefers carry out an appraisal or review 10 days to four weeks later, should it be necessary. This is to assess whether some movement, according to the severity of the incident and the reaction experienced by the survivor/s has taken place since the debriefing. Should the reaction require further intervention, individual supportive counselling may be offered.
- The psychological debriefing should be set up within the first 72 hours but not later than 14 days after the incident. Any further delay can have adverse effects on those involved in the incident.
- In group debriefings, ideally two trauma debriefers should work together within the group.
- A psychological debriefing will continue until the process has been completed.

- Maximum number of participants per session is ten.

CHECKLIST - MANAGEMENT OF DEBRIEFING FACILITIES

		YES	NO
Room	adequate size		
	comfortable ambience		
	lighting		
Chairs	comfortable		
	horseshoe arrangement of seating or similar		
No disturbances or telephone calls			
Mobile telephones switched off			
Drinks	tea		
	coffee		
	cold drinks		
	possibility of food		
Toilet facilities nearby			
Note writing	white board		
	writing materials		
	pens and pencils		
	flip-chart		
Extras	paper tissues		
Handouts - related to possible after-effects			

NO OUTSIDERS WITHOUT GROUP PERMISSION

5

Stress Causes and Consequences

Stress is caused by obstacles in the path of any goal. The level of stress relates to the importance of that goal; how difficult it is to reach and the consequences if it remains unattended.
There are three broad grades of stress:

- ***Short term*** – everyday stimuli that drive us to get things done.

- ***Medium term*** – stress caused by working towards an important target – the pressure rises until the target is achieved or the event occurs.

- ***Long term*** – the worst kind of stress, which can arise from personal or health problems but which is bound to accompany major problems in anyone's professional and private life, especially when their livelihood is threatened.

Some basic stress mechanism can be demonstrated in connection with primitive reactions to sudden serious threat. For example if a major car impact takes place between two vehicles and the accident happens close to the individual, that person can either fight and rescue the situation or run away, but in both instances, energy, strength and endurance will be required. Accordingly the body prepares for maximum readiness by releasing hormones – principally adrenaline – instantly into the blood stream. The heart beats faster, blood pressure rises, nutrients and oxygen are redirected to the muscles where they are most needed (including the heart) at the expense of the digestive processes and other functions redundant for flight or fight.

Reactions such as pallor, (re-routing of blood supply), trembling in the arms and legs (super-toned muscles), nausea (interference with digestion) and a racing heart can be quite noticeable and are indeed very human, particularly if the stimulus threatens to remain unsolved. This may encourage mounting frustration and the body reacts as if to an overt physical warning where the effect is cumulative. There could be raised blood pressure, headache, pale and drawn looks, food aversion and feeling of sickness, lack of concentration and disturbed sleep patterns.

Inability to act positively in order to improve matters requires an awareness of the superfluous adrenaline being generated and its possible consequences. There is a balance between avoiding negative attitudes and feelings, and releasing reasonable emotions.

Jane, who had a very responsible job in the city, had been working towards chairing her first major presentation. After carrying out final checks the night before the meeting, she retired for a good night's sleep.

The following morning, feeling very stressed about the forthcoming presentation, she experienced a series of minor and one major stressful mishap even before leaving the house.

Her last pair of tights developed a run, the dog had chewed a part of the stair carpet which then caused her partner to catch his heel in the hole and fall down several steps. He suffered a bad sprain – all just before Jane's drive to work.

These incidents predominated Jane's already heavily stressed frame of mind which caused a series of pre-load symptoms leading to traumatic stress. Her presentation, when she finally started it, produced feelings of inadequacy, since Jane was unable to shed her pre-load sufficiently to give all her attention to the job in hand.

Jane had no control over the situation which had previously occurred at home and, after checking that her partner was not badly hurt and was receiving attention, shut out for the time being the previously caused stress load and recognised that it was out of her control for the time being.

Individual tolerance varies. Everyone resents distractions when faced with the need to concentrate. Some people are particularly sensitive in this respect and are thrown off balance into phrenetic oscillations of attention between one 'threat' and another. Those who appear to cope well with stressful tasks despite pre- and after-loads are a fortunate few. They are endowed with extra resilience and seem spontaneously able to cast aside other matters until the main task is done.

Acute stress relates to the demands of important events and to the severity of consequences if these demands are not met. Where the possibility of failure in a first aid examination is not forever, this does not apply to real-life activities without second chance opportunities. For example, if there is an urgent need to resuscitate a casualty who has stopped breathing, any do-or-die element is a major stressor.

Stress Loads

Large stresses feed off little ones, swelling the overall effect on mental and physical performance and well being. It pays to recognise three basic stress components. These are known as:

- main load
- pre-load
- after-load.

Thus, in the following example – in the all-important First Aid examination – great demands are made on memory, concentration and on controlled physical activity.

Stress main load

This refers to the pressures which arise **during participation in an important event**.

Stress is fairly intense and some symptoms show up in most would-be First Aiders. If only moderately keyed up, increased hormonal drives may actually contribute to alertness; on the other hand, a pass certificate for testees with low stress threshold may depend as much on the absence of upsetting incidents, such as failing to get enough air into the resuscitation model as on competent demonstration, both practical and verbal of new skills. Tension grows 'normally' as the examination date approaches; caused by having to memorise details of possible medical terminology, the likelihood of getting a 'difficult patient' or complex injury to deal with and, finally, the state of mind and mood of the two examiners.

Stress Pre-Load

This refers to any **unexpected pressures or anxieties which arise shortly before** an event, but are unconnected with it – yet threaten to affect performance and the outcome.

For example, our examinee might receive some very bad news by morning post, some injury or ailment and so on.

Stress After-Load

This is potentially less damaging. The term refers to **worrisome prospects which are expected to occur soon after** the event.

This might be such as an appointment for tooth extraction or any other major stressor. Although the events are scheduled to take place later, thought and worry about them may come to mind during any stage of the First Aid examination and threaten composure and concentration.

The lingering effect of unchallenged pre-loads is likely to compound main-load stress with disruptive feelings like: 'one problem after another' or 'why does this have to happen to me now?' There is a muddle of energy-sapping distractions just as maximum effort is required. Pre-loads are best coped with by being addressed early on and acknowledged as completely independent of the task in hand. It may then be possible to set them aside for the time being.

6

Framework of Trauma Levels

It is important to understand how the effects of trauma can interfere, not only with the well being of individuals, but by seriously disrupting the organisational efficiency and productivity of industry and commerce.

With help from specialist trauma consultants, individual survivors or members of the community will derive much benefit from meaningful educational programmes which can help them to expand their knowledge about trauma and traumatic personality changes and reactions.

The following layered framework provides the foundation for needs assessment relating to the type of intervention which would be required according to the level of trauma.

Level One – Traumatic Reaction (TR)

This suggests a healthy, positive reaction by the individual. Healthy personality development requires constant integration and balancing of often conflicting components of existence. Unhealthy, stagnant, confused, inhibited existence emerges when the integration of meaningful, divergent perspectives breaks down, or traumatic disintegration occurs. **Traumatic reaction** suggests the individual possesses and implements healthy coping mechanisms in dealing with traumatic life experiences, allowing for healthy personality development. The fundamental example of healthy, positive traumatic reaction is the 'slap at birth', causing a traumatic reaction in autonomous functioning and a true transformation of the foetus into the essence of human existence.

Level Two – Traumatic Stress Reaction (TSR)

This relates to the immediate reaction by survivors of overwhelming, often life-threatening traumatic experience/s which may have delayed stress reactions. Although the survivors continue to work through the experience themselves, often professionals and carers are called in to assist in the cathartic and elucidating expression of the experience. These TSR professionals and carers are not providing counselling but support and understanding during the immediate post trauma stage. The provision of a sense of safety to allow survivors to ventilate and validate, as well as predict post trauma possibilities is the primary objective.

Level Three – Post Traumatic Stress Reaction (PTSR)

This is manifested by large numbers of individuals who are not aware of the impact traumatic events have had upon their current life situations. Manifesting symptoms are often depression, anxiety, and substance abuse. The less severe PTSR symptoms are manifested as mistrust, guilt, shame, doubts, existential anxieties, angry outbursts, avoidance of feelings, sleep disturbances and a pervading sense that one's quality of life is somewhat diminished (problematic relationships etc). Although these are normal reactions to abnormal life events, the coping mechanisms of the survivors are less than healthy or mature. Survivors are often quite professionally competent and successful using obsessive-compulsive behaviour, attempting to maintain control of emerging PTSR /PTSD symptoms. However, the quality of life diminishes and the inability to become intimate with others increases as the delayed PTSR symptoms become more severe. The counsellor now becomes actively involved in the process of providing expertise to help the survivor integrate the traumatic event/s into his or her life experience.

Level Four – Post Traumatic Stress Disorder (PTSD)

This is the clinical manifestation of delayed reactions to severe chronic/acute traumatic shock. Severe symptoms emerge and are associated with clinical presentations of PTSD (flashbacks, emotional numbing, intrusive fixated thoughts, avoidance tactics and other severe reactions, all focused on the traumatic experience/s).

Should the survivor show these more severe symptoms, an assessment would be recommended which must be carried out by a qualified counsellor/therapist or a clinical psychologist. There are several diagnostic tools available which are used to establish the presence of PTSD. One was established in the United States: *The Diagnostic and Statistical Manual of Mental Disorders (4th edition revised) – Diagnostic Criteria* – American Psychiatric Association, Washington DC.

The individual undergoing the assessment has to meet four sections of the assessment criteria before PTSD can be diagnosed.

Once it has been established that the individual is suffering from PTSD, it will depend on the type and severity of his or her symptoms. Obviously if the person has turned to drink or drug taking, either prescribed or obtained illegally, it may be necessary to treat the condition at a suitable establishment. Other available help might come in the form of Cognitive Behaviour Therapy which deals with adjustment of the way situations are perceived, Behavioural Therapy for phobias and compulsive disorders, or a fairly recent method concerned with eye movement desensitisation and reprocessing.

The following is an extract from Nursing Times, 1996:

> In 1987 an accidental discovery revealed an association between certain eye movements and reduced levels of distress resulting from traumatic memories. The result was a new psychological intervention, eye movement desensitisation and reprocessing (EMDR) The treatment consists of generating rapid and rhythmic eye movement while simultaneously holding traumatic images, thoughts and emotions in the active memory.

Help may also be obtained from a counsellor who will provide short- or long-term counselling. The number of sessions will depend on the severity of the case and the length of time between the incident itself and when intervention first started.

The last two levels show quite clearly how important it is to seek the right support soon after an incident has taken place so as to avoid the need for rather more lengthy and emotionally draining therapy.

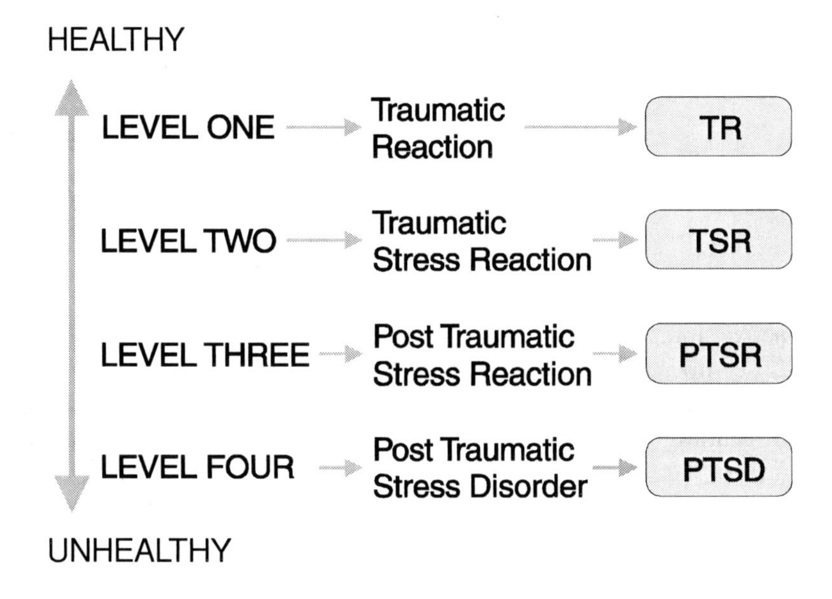

Figure 6: Levels of traumatic reaction (thanks to Dr David Niles)

7

Consequences of Interaction Neglect

Increase of reaction

Pro-active interventions are helpful, especially when dealing with teams set up to help in industrial trauma. The opportunity to help carers be aware of what they may face can bring down anxiety levels. Good training is essential for healthy psychological responses. However, no matter how much training is given, it does not always prepare one for some of the traumas which may be faced. The emergency services were never prepared to meet the carnage of Lockerbie when the plane plummeted into the village.

After the event, it is essential that good psychological debriefing is given. The neglect of this can only cause a build-up of stress which may lie dormant for many years. Then a sight, sound or smell may trigger off a catalogue of reactions and one can find oneself thrown back into the centre of past trauma.

The need to retell the story, to put the 'jigsaw' together for the team which has been interacting is very necessary so that the whole incident can be seen in its logical sequence, helping every one in the group to make sense of the incident.

- It brings the team together, allowing them to hear one another's story thus binding them together.

- It gives them the sense of being 'in it' together.

- It provides an inclusiveness that strengthens them, allowing them to feel a sense of vulnerability and empathy with one another.

This dynamic heals hurts and transforms each member of the team into a richer person who takes responsibility for his or her own needs and reactions, yet is bound together in a common cause. Also a team that is able to go through this process comes out the other side stronger and with a different perspective on life as a whole.

Each individual can never be the same again having now experienced a life-threatening incident. Something new has been learnt from the experience which has changed them and has provided a richer perspective on life as a whole.

If the psychological welfare of the team is not looked after adequately, then the possibility of individual dissociation, denial and other severe reactions may occur in the future.

Management may be able to pick up negative responses related to inappropriate behaviour shown by some of their staff after being affected by the incident. This could apply to some people taking time off work frequently, or could show a deterioration in the quality of their work. This will become apparent from lack of concentration, irritability or aggressive behaviour towards colleagues in the work place. Problems could occur within the family, or with the partner or children.

These are all examples of an underlying cause and they need careful monitoring.

Recognition of disturbing reactions

It is often possible for management to become aware of unusual behaviour shown by some employees who may have experienced trauma. This is often evident when the individual or the group show the following signs:

- mistakes caused through lack of concentration
- excessive drinking, smoking or self-abusive habits – increased drug taking
- depression
- withdrawal from colleagues and social activities
- changes in personal hygiene
- showing signs of irritability or aggression
- absenteeism
- unreliable behaviour
- family problems
- problems with authority figures.

Trauma Resulting in Post Traumatic Stress Disorder

The assessment and types of treatment

Post traumatic stress reaction is the immediate follow-on to a trauma. 'The person has experienced an event that is outside the range of usual human experience and which would be markedly distressing to almost anyone, e.g. serious threat to one's life or physical integrity, serious threat or harm to one's children, partner or other close relatives and friends, sudden destruction of one's home or community or seeing another person who has recently been, or is being seriously injured or killed as a result of an accident or physical violence'. (DSM-IV) These traumatic reactions invariably affect the whole person.

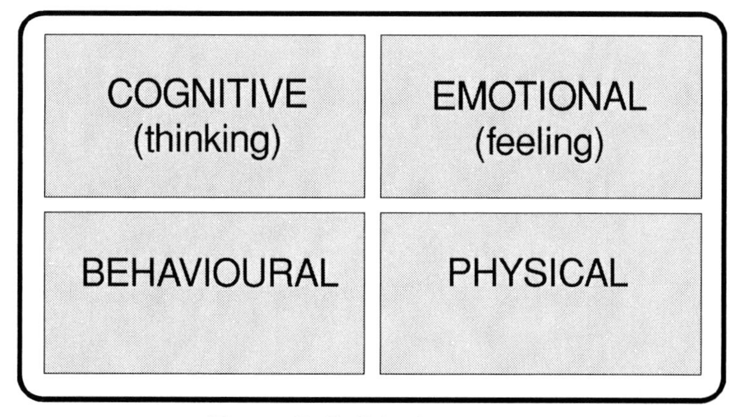

Figure 7. Full body reaction

These symptoms disable the survivor for a short period of time, but it affects all areas of human make up (as fig 7). However, if the reactions are prolonged lasting from approximately three to six months and they affect all four areas (fig 7: cognitive, behavioural, emotional and physical), the clinician concerned can assess that the reactions are above the normal limit: (e.g. inventory IES – Impact of Events Scale) (appendix 4 questionnaire). This will show that the survivor is diagnosed as suffering from Post Traumatic Stress Disorder which is a psychiatric condition. The American Diagnostic Manual, DSM-IV, distinctly classifies the disorder as above.

There are numerous tests that a psychologist, psychiatrist or a clinician can administer to help with the diagnosis of this condition. The following are commonly used.

A **HAD scale (Hospital Anxiety and Depression scale)** – used mainly in accident and emergency hospital departments throughout the UK (appendix 3)

B **IES scale (Impact of Events Scale)** – appearing to be the most widely used (see appendix 4). It contains a series of questions which are scored from one to five: one being the least possible discomfort felt to five being the most possible discomfort experienced. The survivor is asked to complete the questions according to the effect of the discomfort experienced scoring from one to five as they go through the questionnaire. The score will then be counted and compared to a template and allows a hypothesis to be made.

C **Post Traumatic Growth Inventory** – which may be used at the conclusion of trauma treatment. This shows attitude changes after clinical intervention (appendix 5).

D **BRIT (Barnett and Roman Inventory for Trauma)** – this is the authors' assessment questionnaire designed for general practitioners (appendix 6).

Naturally, assessment for post traumatic stress disorder can be diagnosed by the professional during an interview. On the other hand, the therapist who has been working with the survivor has a continued understanding of the survivor's psychological condition and can make a knowledgeable judgement concerning an assessment of his or her psychological state.

There are various ways of working with trauma. The most important component of all is to hear the story as told by the survivor. The contents needs to be told or drawn out in detail. There are different models of doing this – often known as rewind or narrative techniques. The methods consist of gaining the story explicitly and in graphic detail. Rewind is like watching a film on television or at the cinema. The client is asked to view his or her place in the incident and relate in detail what can be seen. The story can be moved forward, stopped, started and rewound in the client's mind. The startling effect is that the client will experience this as though it were happening in the here and now. This technique has the effect of helping the survivor revisit the scene with assured knowledge that he or she survived and is now in the safety of the clinical room. It also helps the process of shifting the material from the front of the brain, the hippocampus, to the base of the brain, the amygdala, where information is stored appropriately. See figure 8.

Another relatively new technique called **EMDR (Eye Movement Desensitisation and Reprocessing)** is yet another model which retraces the story in detail and helps the brain process the information. The difference and perhaps the strength of this technique is that it leads the clinician down other channels of memory, other traumas which perhaps have not been dealt with, therefore one can find the triggers and help reprocess information.

The reprocessing is done by simulating Rapid Eye Movement (REM) sleep patterns. This is the process which the brain goes through automatically while the person is asleep each night, collecting information and storing it in its appropriate place for easy access when needed.

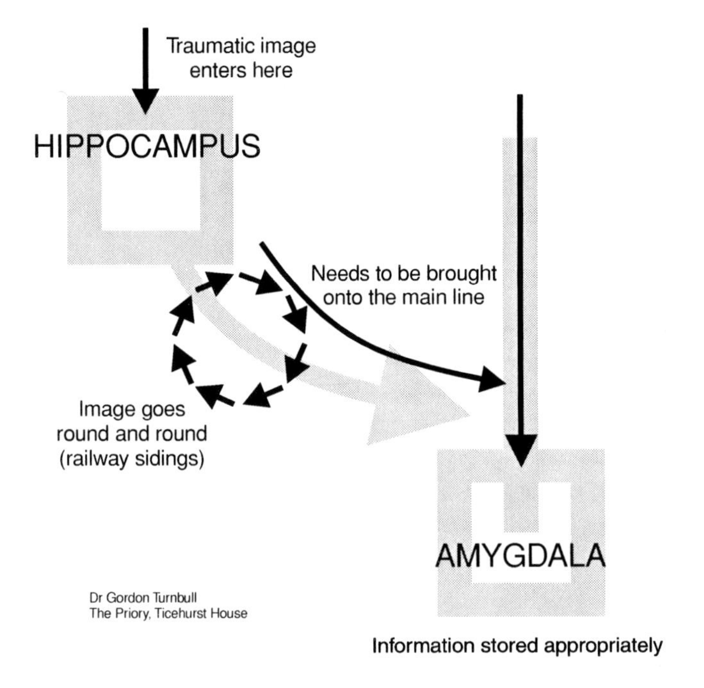

Figure 8: Debriefing process

Cognitive Behavioural Therapy (CBT) is becoming a more widely used model which has been found to be helpful in many cases.

Restructuring beliefs and thoughts can be a useful way in working with trauma.

Relaxation exercises and imagery can be therapeutic along with other exercises in allowing the brain to process information, to relax and give up its constant, repeated going over scenes, noises and images of the trauma in its helter-skelter manner.

Other models - psycho-dynamic (long-term)
Inventories and questionnaires
Intervention, e.g. relaxation, imagery
Narrative, EMDR, TIR etc.
Cognitive Behaviour Therapy - or other appropriate models

Please note that this is NOT a hierarchy of intervention, but just a number of options which are available - the list is not exhaustive.

Figure 9 – Models of Therapy

9

Case Histories in Trauma

Case 1: Traumatic Stress

First Aiders, particularly those who are frequently involved in dealing with serious accidents, i.e. those working as volunteers in one of the emergency services such as St John Ambulance or the Red Cross are regularly exposed to a high degree of human pain and suffering. This exposure has the power to remove their usually effective emotive protections, thereby causing them to undergo significant stress-related problems. In fact, one can compare these traumatic stress problems with those similarly experienced by members of the emergency services such as the Ambulance, Fire service and the Police

Traumatic stress sets off a whole range of disruptive events in people. Some of the more common effects of traumatic stress can cause deterioration in job performance, changes in personality, anxiety conditions, discord in relationships, depression and feelings of isolation.

If traumatic stress reactions remain uncontrolled, this may lead to the development of low morale atmosphere amongst groups of people. Such occurrences may tend to increase the possibility of errors in First Aid diagnosis of the injured – or any other job which requires maximum concentration – and may even urge some volunteers to abandon their support from duties.

In 1980, a newly enrolled member of one of the voluntary services, having passed both the First Aid and Nursing examinations, was asked to take part in a support duty at a major athletic event in South East London. During the sports activities, First Aid personnel were called over the loudspeaker system to render first aid to a casualty in the gents' toilets. On their arrival, the casualty was found to have fallen down two flights of concrete stairs and was lying unconscious at the bottom. He was suffering from a badly gashed head injury and severe bleeding was evident.

The new member took one look at the casually and promptly fainted. Two people now had to be treated although the male casualty took priority. Once the ambulance crew had removed the elderly man to hospital, the new First Aider, who was now in shock, was taken back to the First Aid Post and, on recovering decided to resign from the Brigade.

Further investigation showed that this lady had not realised that the sight of blood would produce such adverse reactions. During a visit to her home some weeks later, she reported that dark red colours made her feel nauseous but that she was slowly coming to terms with it. In fact, she was prescribed tranquilisers by her doctor for a short period.

On-Scene Support

Occasionally, a critical incident is so distressing that carers begin to react immediately they come onto the scene. Individuals or groups might begin to feel overwhelmed by the situation and if this happens, they may show signs of dysfunction while performing crisis response tasks. Such a situation demands immediate intervention by a trained Critical Incident Stress Management team member or a colleague who is not seriously affected by the incident.

This immediate intervention is classified as emotional First Aid. It usually consists of a practical common sense action that removes the distressed individuals from the area and allows them to partially recover from the immediate trauma. Perhaps a change of tasks away from the disaster area and a variety of other restoring techniques may be used by providing on-scene or mid-action support.

Case 2: Attempted suicide

A worker from the assembly plant in a factory had to go to the supply shed to fetch parts required for assembly. The storage for this material was situated in a small yard outside the work area. As he walked across the yard, he noticed a middle-aged man leaning against a concrete garage which housed a supply van. When approaching the man to enquire if help was required, the man said: 'If you come any closer, I'll set myself on fire'. To prove that this was no idle threat, he held up a can of lighter fuel and a box of matches.

The assembly worker immediately made his way to the nearest telephone in one of the offices and called the police, ambulance and fire brigade. On his return journey back to the plant he had to go across the yard and realised that the man had, in fact, set himself alight and was running around the yard screaming hysterically.

The noise had alerted some of the other members of the team who rushed out. The first man out in the yard grabbed hold of some sacking and, after tripping the burning man up in order to get him onto the ground, wrapped him in the sacking to enable him to smother the flames. Since a water supply was fairly near, the rest of the team formed a line and passed water-filled containers along so as to cool the burnt areas of the victim which were mainly on the chest, arms and legs.

The casualty meantime was being reassured by Pat, one of the female employees, who stayed by his side until the emergency services arrived. She did not leave him until he had been moved into the ambulance.

Reactions

The casualty repeatedly requested that Pat accompanied him in the ambulance, which she was very willing to do. However, the ambulance personnel refused his request and Pat was left behind. At this point, she burst into hysterical crying which no-one was able to stop. One of the managers of the department removed her from the yard and talked quietly to her which eventually had the required calming effect. She was then driven home and passed into her husband's care.

After effects

For months after this incident, Pat was unable to set foot in the yard and had recurrent nightmares of the event. She insisted on regular telephone calls being made to the hospital to maintain contact and to assure herself that the injured man was making satisfactory progress. At home, Pat removed all traces of matchboxes and became obsessive about fire, particularly vis-a-vis her two young children who, for a time were forbidden to enter the kitchen without an adult being present and were also prevented from going anywhere near the cooking stove.

Pat was not given any other support nor was she offered counselling and therefore may have been affected by the incident for longer than if she had had some help in making sense of the whole event and her reactions to it. The situation became worse at home and finally affected her family life since her husband could no longer cope with Pat's self-formed phobias. The marriage broke up and eventually Pat decided to move out of the area.

Some fifteen years later, a friend met Pat again and asked how long it had taken her to come to terms with her experience.

Pat confirmed that she was still battling with some of the reactions to the trauma, in particular the smell of burning flesh which, at the time of the incident had been very pungent.

She also reported that her erstwhile interest in cooking exotic food had completely disappeared and that she relied mainly on pre-cooked meals or simple fast dishes which only required warming in the microwave.

When asked why she had not sought help, she replied that she could cope if she shut past thoughts out of her mind. This possibly could all have been avoided and fifteen years of anxiety and traumatic stress dealt with if early intervention had been provided.

Case 3: Trauma after accidents

Reactions at work or in the community

Traumatic incidents involving road traffic accidents, severe injuries in the work place either to colleagues or the general public, possible terrorist explosions, incidents involving children or mass trauma are often initially dealt with by anyone with first aid knowledge, by bystanders or those who possess an instinct to care for those in need.

These carers provide rescue and crisis response for the survivors and possibly their families. But they themselves can also become victims.

Like anyone else in society, the men and women who provide and administer the emergency care have feelings and they too are just as likely to be emotionally affected by traumatic incidents. The way in which this will affect them will vary greatly from person to person but a lot will experience some form of psychological phenomena that occur in the days following the event. These are known as Post Traumatic Stress Reactions. They are not disorders but are quite specific reactions to a traumatic stimulus.

Many of the phenomena involve reliving and re-experiencing what has happened. Vivid flashes of particular scenes may come to mind and intrude into the immediate thinking process. These flashes, often described as flashbacks, are not just thoughts of the incident but actually take the person back into the very scene which they are desperately trying to forget, yet the brain refuses to absorb and deal with it. This means that a reliving of the trauma continues to cause the person great stress over which they have no control. During sleep, nightmares may occur bringing vivid pictures of the incident into the dreams. These experiences may lead to panic and anxiety attacks but should decrease over time both in volume and strength.

Accident in the community

During an official 24 hour ambulance strike, members of the voluntary services were asked to provide cover for victims of accidents. Several people who were able to take time off were assigned to one of the main police stations in the South East of London.

At lunch time, a call came through asking for help in dealing with an accident at a nearby railway station and to remove the casualty to hospital. On board the ambulance were two drivers who were also qualified first aiders, a doctor and a nurse.

Injuries had occurred to a middle-aged male who had been drinking in a nearby pub and had wandered onto the station platform and had overbalanced into the path of an approaching train. Both his legs had been severed above his knees and, after the current had been switched off, the doctor went down onto the track to deal with the casualty's injuries.

Others provided support, helped the doctor and fetched the trolley bed from the ambulance in order to transport the casualty to the A&E department of the local hospital. Unfortunately, pain killing drugs were not an option since the casualty was way over the limit with alcohol intake. However, an intravenous drip was set up and with police traffic control help, the ambulance had a clear drive through from the station to hospital.

A police officer who had followed the ambulance to the railway station had gone down to the track and had picked up the two severed legs, with shoes still in place and had placed them into a clear plastic bag. As the trolley bed was wheeled back to the ambulance, he followed it down the platform, swinging the bag as he walked. The nurse turned to look at him and saw the contents of the bag quite clearly.

Thoughts

She later reported that the wounds of the severed legs did not disturb her in any way; she had seen too much in operating theatres. However, the severed legs produced thoughts of jumping out of the carrier bag and following the casualty down the platform. These thoughts were later re-enacted in dreams and nightmares

Emotions

Despite repeatedly talking the incident through with various people, the nurse was unable to erase the memory of those severed legs in the carrier bag and it took a number of weeks for the nightmares to subside. Physical symptoms persisted for months in the form of anxiety and nausea whenever she came into contact with transparent plastic shopping bags. Her motto remains – check all contents of bags, just in case!

Cognitive and physical stress symptoms

Cognitive

- confusion in thinking
- difficulty making decisions
- loss of attention span
- lowered concentration
- problems with abstract thinking
- calculation problems
- memory dysfunction
- lowering of higher cognitive functions

Physical

- headaches
- increased heart rate
- fatigue
- elevated blood pressure
- excessive sweating
- rapid breathing
- chills
- chest pain
- dizzy spells
- difficulty breathing
- light headaches
- cardiac arrest
- common hysteria
- hunger and thirst

Emotional and behavioural stress symptoms

Emotional

- irritability
- heightened anxiety
- emotional shock
- panic feelings
- emotional numbness
- loss of emotional control
- anger
- fear
- grief
- depression
- feeling overwhelmed

Behavioural

- changes in ordinary behaviour patterns
- increased/decreased association with fellow workers
- withdrawal from others
- changes in eating patterns
- loss of interest in work
- decreased personal hygiene
- prolonged silences

Not everyone will experience the post traumatic reactions described. Some people seem protected by past experience or other defences. Usually for those not so severely exposed, the experience of distressing intrusions settles relatively rapidly, lasting perhaps a few days to a few weeks, depending on the seriousness of the incident. For most people, the reaction settles within four to six weeks.

Disturbances to sleep can be quite distressing. At the same time, the anxiety, irritability and general distress accompanying post traumatic reactions and the urge to shed the load of the incident may interfere with inter-personal relations, work concentration and smooth inter-action with relatives.

Fortunately the nurse involved in the rescue operations was able to share her thoughts and feelings with colleagues who worked with her in voluntary first aid activities. They frequently listened to the repeated reactions. Eventually, through the desensitising process of continued repetition, the nightmares gradually faded.

The reactions have been dealt with but the memory of the incident remains – but it no longer has such a disturbing effect.

Case 4: Accident in the workplace

On a main-line station in London, an invalid – a stroke victim – leaving the train on arrival had to be assisted off the train and transported by buggy to a waiting vehicle.

The station and platform at that time were undergoing major repair and renovation and extensive scaffolding had been erected.

Tony, the buggy driver, had helped the invalid off the train and into the buggy. Since the stroke had affected the passenger's leg, which was very stiff, his foot protruded slightly out of the buggy.

As Tony turned the buggy round, the foot was caught by some scaffolding and this caused a severe gash on the back of the leg. This was not identified until Tony had driven through the barriers of the platform and was stopped by a station police officer who noticed heavy bleeding. The officer immediately applied pressure and the invalid was taken to the First Aid Post.

When Tony examined the buggy to make sure that all belongings had been removed, he noticed an excessive amount of blood on the floor. Tony was very shocked by this sight and management decided to send him home.

After effects

For the next two months, Tony reported very disturbed sleep which was interspersed with nightmares. He also experienced withdrawal symptoms which in turn affected his family. He received no help in order to come to terms with the incident and for the next six months examined every buggy carefully before taking it anywhere on the station in case it contained blood.

Tony's frustration at having caught the passenger's foot and having caused injury, left him feeling inadequate and guilty. The responsibility for the passenger's well-being had been left in his hands which caused Tony to question his ability to deal adequately with the transportation of disabled customers.

Tony eventually decided to take First Aid training and has learnt to ask many more relevant questions before giving support to invalids leaving trains.

Case 5: Trauma in children

Sarah, aged twelve and living on the Continent during the early part of her life, was standing at the window of her apartment, looking down on the main dual carriageway of the street where her block of apartments stood. She had a clear view of the tram-lines in the centre of the dual carriageway which served transport to local venues.

The time was mid-day and traffic was rather heavy. Pedestrians were also out and about, some crossing the road from time to time. Sarah enjoyed the hustle and bustle. Suddenly she heard a screech of brakes and witnessed very clearly a woman being thrown into the air through impact from an oncoming car. The woman screamed loudly and, through the impact with the car, was catapulted into the path of an approaching tram. The second impact was much more severe and subsequently killed the casualty.

Crowds very quickly gathered and, in order to hide the body from view, someone had placed a hessian sack over the deceased which was lying underneath the tram, while waiting for an ambulance to arrive.

Sarah waited for quite a while at the window, her attitude being one of floating in suspension. Eventually the ambulance arrived and removed the body. Sarah did not move from the window until all bystanders and police had gone. She then moved to an armchair where she sat and stared at the patterned carpet until, half an hour later her mother found her.

Thoughts and Reactions

Sarah was unable to think or react to questions from her mother who did not know what had happened. After continued questions, Sarah finally burst into tears and appeared inconsolable. She was still unable to give any rational information or stop crying, eventually becoming hysterical.

Eventually the doctor was called and he decided to put Sarah to bed and gave her a tranquillising injection which allowed her to sleep for approximately twenty-four hours.

Symptoms

When Sarah finally woke up, the Doctor was once more called and, despite a thorough examination and many questions, she showed no after-effects apart from the fact that she had no memory of the incident at all. Even a report in the newspaper failed to remind her of the scene she had witnessed. It was assumed that the long sleep had achieved normality and had allowed Sarah to overcome her trauma, therefore nothing further was done about it.

Sarah carried on with her life and attended school every day. Since she had to take the tram to reach school which was some distance away, she started to leave a little earlier every morning and board the tram one stop beyond her normal stop. No-one took much notice of this new habit and Sarah carried on with it until she left the Continent to live in England.

Further Reaction

Some two years after settling down in the UK, Sarah joined the Girl Guides and that summer was invited to take part in a week's camping holiday. Since she enjoyed the company of her new friends, she agreed to take part and they left in coaches for the camping site, accompanied by two Guide Leaders.

> On arrival, everyone was allocated a place in a tent and each was given a hessian sack which had to be filled with straw to act as a base for the sleeping bags. As soon as Sarah looked at and handled the sack, her memory of the past incident returned and she broke down in floods of tears. She discarded the sack and quickly left the tent walking as far away as possible from the scene

Teaching and Re-entry

At first it was thought that Sarah was suffering from home sickness but, luckily, one of the leaders sensed that Sarah's outburst contained some deeper reasons and after replacing the hessian sack with a camp bed she spent time talking with Sarah and finally managed to persuade her to talk about the past incident.

Sarah continued to talk about her experience after her return from the camping trip. She even managed to join in with some of the activities with her companions.

Although the leader of the guides had no formal knowledge or training of Sarah's condition, instinct told her that the girl needed someone to support her.

Sarah will never forget the incident but she has learnt to live with it and recognise that she was in no way responsible for any of its consequences. Future decisions led her to become a nurse and subsequently develop her career and qualify in trauma support counselling.

Case 6: The Moorgate tube disaster

The Moorgate tube disaster happened in the early 1970s and, as is usual in national disasters, many caring organisations make themselves available to the authorities. Their task is to work with the emergency services, helping to provide refreshments or working with families, transport or any other necessary support.

> On the evening of the Moorgate tube disaster, Fred was contacted by a national organisation for whom he worked and was asked to present himself at Moorgate in order to assist with providing refreshments for the emergency services.

One of the most common characteristics in any major disaster is pre-attendance anxiety produced by the surprise element in the call-out procedure from the line manager. This immediately kicks in the adrenaline rush which then causes adverse reactions, i.e.

- Palpitations
- Nausea
- Headache
- Dizziness
- Hyper Activity
- General Anxiety
- Hyper-ventilating – breathing too quickly and deeply
- Anxiety re coping – 'will I be able to do the job?' etc.

Usually, good training before an incident about what to expect and what the role of the carer will entail should bring some of these reactions down. Adverse coping mechanisms which may affect the helper could be: 'will the police allow me through the barrier?' or 'where will I be able to park?' In situations like this, the brain will often concoct negative thoughts, showing a certain reluctance to carry on with the job.

> The emergency services were having problems with heat etc, since the electricity supply to the station had had to be turned off. Arc lights and cutting machinery were being used to free survivors from the wreckage. The atmosphere was hot and claustrophobic.

Fred's refreshment stand was situated on the level above the incident and he could therefore hear the whirr of the cutting machinery, the calls and shouts of the emergency services and could smell the thick acrid smell of sulphur hanging in the air. Whenever fire crew and the police came to Fred's refreshment stand to quench their thirst, they talked about their part in the incident and their impressions of sights and sounds. Fred listened and took all of this in. Body bags – black plastic bags containing bodies – passed Fred's stand from time to time as the emergency workers took victims to the surface.

At 4am, roughly 5-6 hours into Fred's shift, a message was passed to him asking him to go to the hospital where his wife was giving birth to their baby. The birth was premature and complicated since the baby had developed a respiratory problem and required incubation. Fred was told that the next 48 hours were crucial for his baby son.

Fred had now gone from a major disaster to a personal trauma. At no time did he receive any support, counselling, debriefing or in fact any kind of help.

The outcome of these closely following incidents was for Fred to turn off psychologically. This is an unconscious reaction which enables the individual to cope with continual crises. In Fred's case, it was his body's way of coping with ongoing trauma. This can also be described as a form of dissociation, normally a coping mechanism learned at a very early age of life to survive the consequences of continual trauma.

However, twenty years later, Fred was inappropriately thrown back into the horror of the Moorgate tube disaster.

Fred and his family had moved to Sheffield some time after the Moorgate incident and, in due course he was again asked by the same organisation to help, on this occasion at the Hillsborough football disaster, this time working in the mortuary with families looking for relatives.

On entering the football ground, Fred was suddenly transported back in his mind to Moorgate. The sensation was almost like a time-slip. Fred saw vivid pictures of body bags and fire crew chatting around his refreshment stall telling their stories. Once again he smelled the thick, acrid stench of sulphur present at the Moorgate crash.

The trauma over the years had not gone away but had remained dormant at the back of Fred's mind. Stress is cumulative. In this instance it had built up over the years and had once more re-appeared at the sight of the carnage.

Good after-care can help in the unburdening process from a build-up of reactions The opportunity to relate the 'story' from the survivor's perspective in the area of work they were involved in can help to free the individual from inappropriate reactions.

At the end of each stint working in such difficult circumstances, it is wise to call the team together for an informal end-of-shift defusing, possibly over a cup of coffee or tea. It is of great benefit for carers to share with team members what they have been involved in during their shift. It enables them to rid themselves of information which is not always helpful. However, this should not be seen as a debriefing. A professional psychological debrief will allow the individual to review the overall story which will help to make sense of the small fragments of the incident of involvement. It will enable the survivor to achieve an ending around this experience and move on.

Case 7: Attempted sexual physical molestation

Susan worked in a paper producing company which, apart from offices, had several large warehouses holding stock. Susan was well used to paying visits to the warehouse to check on stock or fetch supplies for the office.

On this particular occasion, she had to spend more time than usual collecting and checking. She noticed that there was no-one in the building with her which was very unusual since people were always in and out of the place, either delivering or collecting.

Susan continued to push her trolley round the various racks, filling it as she walked from aisle to aisle. Suddenly she heard a noise behind her and, before she could turn round to see who was there, two arms came round her, feeling her body from the back.

No-one came to her aid despite her shouts of protest. However, her attacker bears the scar of that encounter to this day as she had the presence of mind to bring the heel of her shoe into sharp and painful contact with his shin. Her attacker let go and Susan ran off to the foreman who was in a separate office and insisted that the incident be recorded in the Accident Book since she felt sure that her attacker would need medical attention.

After returning to her office, she began to feel dizzy and found it very hard to concentrate on her work. Apart from the foreman who had entered the incident in the book and helped her to get back to her office, no-one knew anything about the incident and, because Susan felt that she should not make further fuss, she waited until the end of the afternoon and then drove home. She also made her husband who worked in the same organisation promise not to say anything to anyone about the incident.

Susan continued to come to work but refused to use the canteen for lunch. She found it impossible to go near the warehouse and insisted that someone else went in her place. Eventually the story leaked out and Susan began to feel better. It was a relief to let everyone know that the injury she had caused her attacker was her way of showing that she was not going to tolerate such behaviour.

People have been known to leave their jobs because of the unacceptable attitude and behaviour of a colleague or even the boss and no one really knows how widespread the problem is or how much trauma it can produce. It is often easier to run than engage in open conflict.

Case 8: The car crash

It was two o'clock in the morning and Natasha, who had spent the evening with friends was driving home. Her cassette player was repeatedly playing her favourite song and she was singing along with the music.

Natasha noticed that the car was becoming stuffy and she opened the window to let in some fresh air. Thoughts of stopping went through her mind since she felt very tired but she decided to press on.

The next thing Natasha remembers is that she opened her eyes and found a heavy weight on her chest. She found it difficult to breathe and since her seat-belt was also causing her constriction she panicked. Her tongue swept over her teeth in order to make sure that these were intact when she heard a voice telling her that she had been involved in an accident and that she should put a coat over her face as they intended to smash in the front window.

Once the window was removed, Natasha insisted on climbing out of her car by herself and asked someone to phone her aunt and uncle. While she waited for them to arrive, she put her hand on her face which felt very hot and realised that it was also wet and swollen.

Realisation set in at that point that she might be scarred for life and, while waiting for the ambulance she huddled down, hugging her cardigan as a comfort blanket.

Eventually the family arrived and Natasha began to feel panic once more. She remembers one sentence going through her mind over and over: 'Oh my God, it must be serious, I am going to be disfigured'.

The ambulance arrived and took Natasha to the nearest hospital A&E department and, after initial examination she was moved to a hospital ward. Meantime, her parents had arrived which did not improve Natasha's emotional state. Her thoughts began to turn to an accident which happened to a friend some years ago during which the girl was killed. This played on her mind, so much so that her 'O' level results which her aunt told her about did not seem very important at the time.

Natasha had a intravenous drip put into each of her arms which, as she reported, were excruciatingly painful. The injury to her face –

> between her eyes – required an operation which was carried out the following day after which Natasha was violently sick, something she had never experienced and which left her with a fear of repetitions.
>
> Natasha was constantly aware of how her face would look and repeatedly asked staff and doctors whether she would remain scarred. No one would give her a straight answer. The following day she was allowed to go home and refused to talk to anyone about her accident. She continued to be worried about her looks.
>
> The police who interviewed her soon after the accident told her that she was very lucky to be alive and that her car was a total write-off. She had told them that she must have fallen asleep at the wheel and had smashed into a lamp post.

After her return home the whole situation suddenly hit her hard. Her uncle took her to the police station where the car had been removed to, so that she could collect some personal belongings. When she saw the state of the car, it shocked her even further. She removed the tape which had been playing during her drive home and several blood-soaked things which she placed in a plastic bag and refused to discard. She also refused to listen to the song for over two months.

Natasha eventually started to drive another car but insisted that the window remain open and that there were no restrictions preventing her from getting out of the car quickly if she felt the need.

At this time, she began to practice ritualistic behaviour patterns, such as getting in and out of the car in a sequential manner. This also applied to her nightly preparations before going to sleep. If this ritual was altered in any way, she would panic and would have to start the whole process of bed preparations again.

Natasha now began to realise that she needed help, since she now had nightmares and very vivid flashbacks, particularly re-experiencing the car's impact with the lamp post. She also refused to acknowledge any car crashes, either by being told about them or reading about them in the newspapers. Eventually, after a visit to her GP, she was referred to a behavioural therapist who unfortunately was not trained in trauma work and Natasha reported that she felt very frustrated that he never managed to get her beyond the real presenting problem. She decided not to continue with this treatment and tried to cope on her own which did not improve matters.

Eventually she was able to get a psychological trauma assessment during which she began to be able to make sense of the incident and the reactions she was experiencing.

Natasha has been making steady progress since her assessment and has realised that the reactions which she struggled with were normal in every way. The accident will always remain in her mind but its after-effects have changed her outlook to a very large extent.

Her face has healed and, unless someone knew of her injuries, it would be impossible to recognise that anything was amiss. Her ritualistic behaviour has also ceased to a large degree. Her attitude now is that if it feels comfortable to do things in a certain sequence and it does not become obsessive, it hurts no one to continue, least of all herself.

Obsessive behaviour after trauma is sometimes quite common as it is about regaining control. Trauma is about chaos and being out of control. Therefore the survivor finds him- or herself seeking control, usually in inappropriate ways.

Case 9: Rape

Rape is a particularly horrific experience for both sexes, with far-reaching physical and psychological after-effects. It is a major violation which can make the victim feel unclean, unsafe, insecure, guilty and extremely vulnerable.

In the case of a female who may or may not have experienced sexual contact before, it may cause physical damage which, in later years may even contribute to preventing her from bearing children. Both men and women usually feel totally violated.

Unfortunately, society so often fails to support the rape victim who is often made to feel that they are responsible for the incident and in some way even invited the attack. Naturally, the authorities need to investigate the facts of the case which may leave the victim feeling they are undergoing a further violation.

It may well be that psychological debriefing, because of its intensity, and possibly seeming like interrogation, can also cause further turmoil. For that reason, an assessment with ongoing counselling sessions may be offered to victims of rape. Research suggests that a same-sex counsellor is important since the details of the incident need to be looked at in an explicit way.

Jane was walking home from a visit to the cinema at midnight one summer evening. Several friends who had been with her for the film performance had walked with her but finally had turned off to make their way to their own homes. Jane decided to take a shortcut down a narrow street. As she walked, she heard footsteps behind her and decided to increase her walking speed.

Suddenly she felt herself being gripped from behind and felt a knife near her neck. She was dragged behind the hedge of a private house and told not to make a sound or 'she would be dead!' Jane froze. The lower part of her clothing was then ripped off and she was raped at knife point. After a final warning not to make a sound or tell anyone what had happened, she was left half-naked, shivering, frightened and confused. Some time later, a pedestrian heard her whimpering and called the police.

> At the station, she was taken into a private room and a police chaperone was allocated to her case. Her clothes were removed and she was given other garments. Jane received care and support from the chaperone but was very reluctant to make a statement since the rapist had threatened her with violence if she 'talked'.
>
> Jane was subsequently examined by one of the police doctors and, after giving the chaperone a very meagre account of the incident, she was finally taken home where she proceeded to bathe incessantly.

Jane began to experience sleepless nights during which she constantly went over the same scene of her attack. When she finally slept, she had vivid nightmares from which she woke bathed in perspiration. She became reluctant to leave her home unless she was accompanied by someone she knew well.

Jane was finally persuaded to see her G.P. who arranged some counselling for her where, falteringly and extremely slowly, she began the painstaking task of relating and re-living the experience.

Male rape can in some ways be characterised differently. Men find it difficult to come forward and report what has happened to them psychologically. They may feel that not only have they been violated but that their masculinity has been threatened. They may have found that they have been unable to defend themselves against other males – and their strength is in question. In some instances, there may be strong denial that the incident ever happened, in fact the victim will dissociate himself from it altogether.

Unfortunately, as has already been stated, stress is cumulative and it is therefore possible at some stage later in life that a male/female relationship may go through a bad patch and, because the male sees his partner as the more dominant part of the team, the earlier trauma could be resurrected. Unless this is re-addressed, this person may continue to suffer from feelings of diminished masculinity.

MYTH	REALITY
A women who gets raped usually deserves it, especially if she has agreed to go to a man's house or quiet car-park with him.	No one deserves to be raped. Being in a man's house or car does not mean that a women has agreed to have sex with him.
If a women allows a man to pay for dinner, buy the drinks and so on, then it means she owes him sex.	Sex is not an implied pay-back for dinner or other expense no matter how much money has been spent.
Acquaintance rape is committed by men who are easy to identify as rapists.	Women are often raped by seemingly 'normal' acquaintances.
Women who don't fight back haven't been raped.	Rape occurs when one is forced to have sex against one's will, whether they have decided to fight back or not.
Intimate kissing or certain types of touching means that intercourse is inevitable.	Everyone's right to say 'no' should be honoured, regardless of the activity which preceded it.
Once a man reaches a certain point of arousal, sex is inevitable and they can't help forcing themselves upon a women.	Men are capable of exercising restraint in acting upon sexual urges.
Most women lie about acquaintance rape because they have regrets after casual sex.	Acquaintance rape really happens to people you know, by people you know.
Women who say 'no' really mean 'yes'.	This notion is based on rigid and outdated sexual stereotypes.
Certain behaviours such as drinking or dressing in a sexually appealing way make rape the woman's responsibility.	Drinking or dressing in a sexually appealing way are not invitations for sex.

Case 10: Sexual Abuse

Chas, a 35 year old man working for a television company was referred to me through an organisation, after a work review with management showed that he had an attitude problem and was behaving somewhat aggressively. Chas appeared to have a passive aggressive introvert personality. He was having problems with line management. He felt they were picking on him, but when we looked at what Chas was presenting in the counselling room, we discovered that Chas had a problem with authority figures. We contracted for six sessions as this was the required amount sanctioned by the company who gave me the assignment. I worked in a solution-focused model. I needed to help him move forward and shift the negative behaviour quickly. For this reason, I used cognitive behavioural therapy and restructuring of his thought patterns, to work towards change.

On the penultimate session, Chas told me that he had been physically abused by his father. I had already begun to wonder about sexual abuse, but he had not confided in me as yet and I certainly did not want to put the thought in his head. However, he told me that his father would beat him severely, especially during fits of drunken rage. On the final session, he told me he had also been abused sexually by his elder brother. Chas came from a large family of five sisters and two brothers. In this session, a choice had to be made about going further into counselling. I had to give him some choices relating to other therapists in the area. He rang me mid-week and made a further appointment with the view to re-contracting with me to work through the abuse. There had already been some significant change in his behaviour at work, enough for the company to pay half towards his future counselling. They saw this as a good investment, as Chas was an excellent worker with management possibilities.

In the following weeks he confided in me that the brother who had abused him was in prison on a manslaughter charge, a sister was in a psychiatric hospital, and other members of the family had problems with communication and relationships.

The way we worked was to get a small amount of the story at a time, about as much as he could cope with. It was very painful for him; he used an image which was extremely powerful, causing him physical pain and anxiety. This image was of a 'cauldron'. To face the cauldron and peer inside caused him intense physical pain, such as racing heart (palpitations), headaches and physical sickness. There was also a lot of shame for him. Shame is a characteristic part of ourselves. It is a primal part, usually pre-language or pre-verbal. It is an image, a picture or a shape, which is a negative part of ourselves that usually causes us pain and guilt which in turn affects our self-esteem. Over the next few weeks, Chas and I took the image of the cauldron and began to look and see what was inside it.

Chas's brother was quite a lot older, and he felt very much in his brother's awe. He felt as if he had no choice regarding the abuse and that he was far too young and small to do anything. His parents colluded in the abuse in that they left the younger children in the charge of the elder brother. Chas was ambivalent towards his parents, but there was, as he saw it, always the possibility that things would change and get better. Chas saw in the cauldron the fear of his own sexuality. He felt awkward in the presence of women and did not know what to say, yet he liked them and felt excited by some women. However, he was aggressive towards older men whom he saw as his dominant father figure, hence his problems at work.

The sessions were painful and charged with anger. As Chas gained confidence and trust in me, he revealed more of his personal trauma. It was a painstaking task over a period of 18 months to two years before Chas felt strong enough to leave me and feel that he had started on a new journey.

During the last weeks of our sessions, Chas met a young lady and eighteen months later married her. The change at work was significant. Chas was promoted and sent to another station. He settled down, now able to leave the past behind him. The 'cauldron' had been looked at and delved into – the significant image had been faced and Chas was able to move on.

There are three core areas when dealing with trauma of any kind. avoidance, arousal and recall. Chas had been trapped in these areas for a significant part of his life thus far. He had learnt to avoid intimate relationships and his behaviour as noted at work was irritable and aggressive. He felt shameful, guilty and had little self-esteem. (see figure 9.)

It was because of the change in his behaviour which management became aware of that set him on his journey to recovery and a different response to the world.

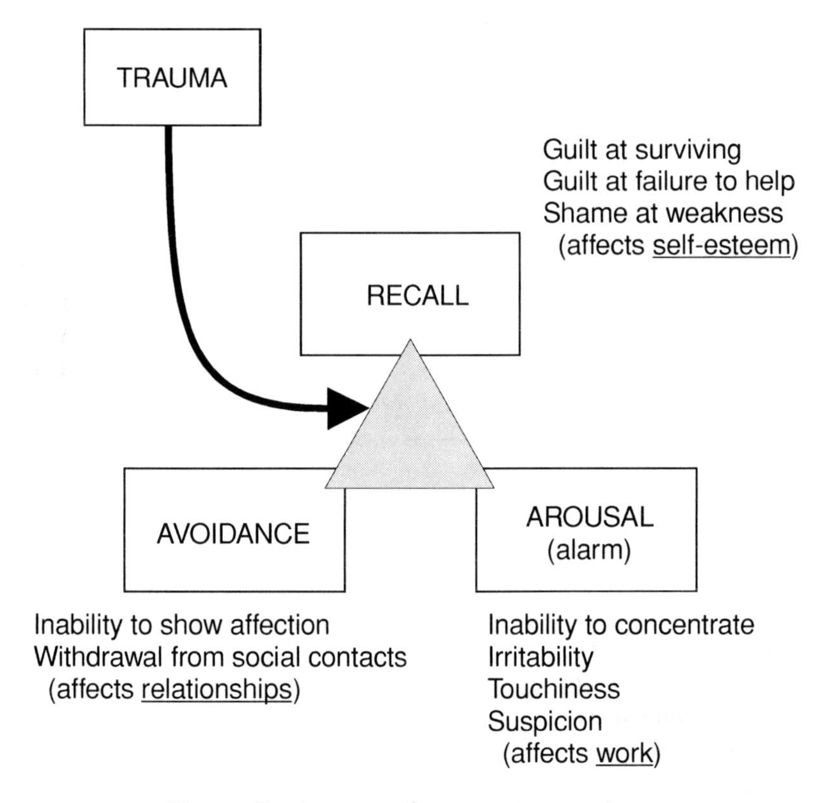

Figure 7 - Aspects of traumatic experience

Case 11: Stress Loaded Accident

In a previous chapter, reference was made to stress loads and the following example which was experienced by a woman police officer shows how stress loads can affect thoughts, feelings physical characteristics and behaviour.

Heavy stress tends to dominate. The greater its pressures, the less one is inclined to consider other things. It takes an effort of will to break out long enough and resolutely enough to discriminate about extra loads and to re-classify their priorities. But this does pay dividends. It is somewhat like being pinned to the ground under a heavy weight. If the weight consists of a heavy boulder, it may not be possible to raise it. If, on the other hand, the same weight is made up of a smaller boulder and loose rubble, release may be possible after removing some of the little stones first. In this particular case the police officer was able to produce her own remedy which eventually released her from a major stress load. She did however refuse the professional help which was offered after the incident. This may have prolonged her traumatic reactions.

While on night duty patrolling the area in her car, a policewoman became aware of a car with five teenage girls inside, being driven in a very haphazard fashion down a narrow country lane. There were numerous sharp bends which were being negotiated in a dangerous manner.

The road was wet due to heavy rain and the driver seemed unable to straighten the car sufficiently to stay on her side of the road.

The officer, who followed the girls, then witnessed the driver losing control and smashing the car into a stone wall. The officer put up the necessary warning lights and then stood frozen to the ground, not able to move for about thirty seconds.

One of the girls had not worn her seat belt and had sustained serious head injuries by being catapulted through the back window. The others were also injured and there was not a sound to be heard.

Thoughts

The police officer's first thoughts on looking at the aftermath was: 'God, no-one could come out alive after that".

Reactions

The officer's first reaction was to be violently sick. After this was over and she had pulled herself together, she radioed for help and then walked up to the back window in order to make sure that her first impression was correct. She was still convinced that there would be no signs of life.

Behaviour

Once at the car, she called out, asking if anyone could hear her and the injured girl answered her. On looking into the car she found it covered with blood from the sustained injuries which again caused another bout of vomiting. At this stage another police vehicle arrived and, soon after that an ambulance which dealt with the removal of the casualties to hospital.

The WPC drove home but has no recollection of the journey. Once at home, she broke down completely, then went to bed and was able to sleep for a long period.

After she arrived at the station the next day and reported the incident, she was offered counselling by her chief but refused the offer. She claimed that she was 'O.K' after a good night's sleep and would be able to cope.

Her colleagues, who had followed her to the scene of the accident reported that the driver and three of the passengers had died but the girl who had been thrown out of the back window was in a critical condition on life-support.

After ten days of nightmares during which the officer saw hearses pulling the injured girl away from the scene of the crash, she decided to go to the hospital to assure herself that the girl was still alive. She found that although still in a critical condition, the medical team reported that she would eventually recover. The nightmares stopped after the hospital visit.

Individual tolerance to trauma varies. Those who appear to cope well with stressful tasks are the fortunate few. They are endowed with extra resilience and seem spontaneously able to cast aside other matters until the main task is done. However, even trained professionals who come across seriously traumatic events can be as vulnerable to the stresses of the events as anyone else. It will take time for such people to steady themselves after an event, and they may well benefit from help and counselling.

Case 12: Hillsborough

On a Saturday afternoon at approximately 3.30pm, I turned on the television and discovered from a news bulletin that there had a been a horrendous disaster at the local Hillsborough football ground some twenty miles from where I lived. It was not long after seeing the news flash that our telephone rang. It was my line manager asking if I could make my way to Hillsborough to give support and help at the incident.

I clambered into my car, adrenaline pumping through my body, and began to make my way to Sheffield and Hillsborough football stadium. There were anxieties which had quickly come into my mind like, 'can I talk my way through the police barriers which will have been erected' and 'will I be able to cope?' Now that the adrenaline had surged through my system and the excitement of the moment was abating, I began to think about the work ahead. This was no new situation for me – I had been present as a helper at the Moorgate tube disaster some 15 years previously and I had some idea about what was ahead.

Approaching Hillsborough, the traffic became heavy as back-up rescue crews were making their way towards the incident. I had no difficulty in getting through the barrier, my identity badge allowing me access. My initial fears abated and I proceeded to the briefing point.

On meeting up with my team co-ordinator, I was briefed and sent to work at the Hallamshire Hospital in the Accident and Emergency Department as this was where the mortuary was going to be situated and I was asked to help the families that were going to be present.

Time went by and no one appeared. Eventually I sought out someone who could give me some information to discover that my team and I and the hospital had been used as a press decoy. Naturally we were angry. I reported back to my line manager and was sent home and asked to return the next morning to the 'New Mortuary' just off Langsett Rd, where I would be working with families who were going to be brought to the mortuary for identification purposes.

The following morning I arrived along with two colleagues at the mortuary to be met by press and the police. My colleagues and I were escorted into the building where we where briefed by a Chief Inspector of Police.

We were told that families and social workers were at that time being brought across the Pennines from Liverpool on a coach to identify and find their loved ones.

The identification process was a harrowing experience. On arrival at the mortuary, the families were allotted a social worker and a member of the clergy to be with them whilst they went through the process. The visit by the family I was involved with lasted six hours from arrival to departure – a draining and exceedingly stressful experience.

I was placed with a family whose son had been killed at the football stadium. The family was interviewed firstly by social workers. They were then taken to a room where a board with many pictures was displayed, consisting of horrific photographs of people who had died through crush injuries or suffocation. The family were then asked which photograph showed the missing member of their family. After this traumatic vigil, they were then given a cup of tea and the opportunity to compose themselves while preparations were made to locate the body and then prepare it for family viewing. The family was then taken into a viewing room where identification was completed after which they were allowed to say farewell to their loved one.

After this they were taken upstairs for a further interview with the police. On completion of this process they were driven back to Liverpool but were asked to return later for the inquest.

For the carer/helper, the whole process was drawn out and in the end became a nightmare. Vivid images of the deceased flipped through one's mind like pages of a photograph album. Sounds of crying relatives played on one's mind, and the smell of sweet artificial air-freshener was constantly in one's nostrils so that the smell became part of you!

After the incident, debriefing was offered but unfortunately in the late 1980s only a taster was given. I shared the so-called debrief with over one hundred other people.

It was important for me to visit the football ground and get a sense of the atmosphere that was enshrined there. It was also important for me to see and make a special journey to my grown-up children, to hug them, and make myself physically aware that they were alive and well, although I knew that they had not been at the match.

10

Support after Debriefing

Many people who have been involved in a critical incident and have received help within the first two weeks of the trauma will begin to feel the benefit after two to three weeks. Life will once again be manageable and, although the incident will begin to fade in its intensity, it will never be forgotten.

Research has shown that, with specialist help, the survivors gain a deeper understanding of their own internal psychological mechanism and their coping method increases in strength.

Some, however, possibly because the traumatic event was very severe, will be unable to continue to work through some of the reactions brought to the surface during the debriefing session on their own. This group may require some additional support which is usually provided in the form of support counselling, anything from one to six individual one-hour sessions. This additional help is always given on a one-to-one basis, usually starting a week to ten days after the debriefing and continuing weekly.

This additional support can in many cases help to prevent further impact on a wider range of people such as family, friends or work colleagues. If the traumatic reaction prevents the individual from continuing to work, it would eventually have an adverse effect on the family who might have to rely on financial support.

Post Traumatic Stress – Self Help

Once professional support has ceased, there are other methods which can be used and which prove to be very therapeutic. Managing stress is more than just coping. It is learning to cope adaptively and effectively. It is nearly as important to know what not to do as what to try. Many people's first response to stress would be to light a cigarette or reach for a drink. These are ineffective ways of coping which, in the long run, do nothing to solve the cause of the stress and only add further problems.

There can hardly be a person in the country who is not aware of the dangers involved in smoking. Although smoking is decreasing among men, it is rising among women, teenagers and children. Indeed, the age for starting smoking is getting younger and younger. Although it may bring a superficial sense of relief and calmness, it in fact sets off its own stress reaction by introducing nicotine into the bloodstream. Tars and resins are carried to the lungs, decreasing their efficiency. As a result of smoking, both adrenaline and noradrenaline are released, thus compounding the physical effects of the body.

As psychological stress increases, so does smoking. Giving up smoking is the only sensible thing to do but this is not always easy. If smoking is closely tied to traumatic stress reaction, then learning to deal with the stress in a more adaptive way may make giving up smoking easier if it is taken as a second step.

Some people smoke when they are bored as something to do to pass the time, or a way of introducing something pleasurable and stimulating into the situation. Dealing with the root cause of the boredom or doing something which is less likely to kill are better ways of handling the problem. Many people would be horrified at the idea of taking drugs to manage traumatic stress – nevertheless they happily light up a cigarette. It should be borne in mind that nicotine itself is a powerful and very fast acting drug.

Food and what it consists of can be contributory to certain illnesses. For example, a diet high in animal fats seems to be linked with coronary heart disease. Where high stress levels are concerned, a balanced healthy diet is important if a healthy body is to be maintained which can withstand it, but it is rather the behavioural aspects of eating which are likely to be affected. Some people eat less or almost stop eating under psychological stress; others eat more, reaching out for their own particular 'comfort food'.

A good diet is important. Food that produce endorphins and serotonin in the body are useful ingredients for helping in the feel-good factor. Fish, white meat, Marmite and even Mars bars (be careful with the chocolate) are helpful in the production of brain and nerve chemistry.

Both groups of eaters need to be aware of the nature of their problem and take steps to overcome it. If the difficulty is NOT wanting to eat and this feeling lasts more than a day or two, then a light diet (as in cases of feeling unwell or after a bout of flu) may well help to regain the appetite. Little and often rather than large heavy meals should be the order of the day.

Being under stress can also cause missed meals, eating on the move or bolting food. An occasional missed meal is not going to hurt anyone but becoming irritable and impatient as a result of lowered blood sugar means that judgement may be less acute thereby causing more stress, and efficiency is also likely to be impaired

Overwork is more likely to be considered as a cause for stress rather than a way of coping, but many people try to cope with the problem by working longer and longer hours. 'If only I could catch up', they believe, 'everything would be all right'. But it rarely is, because, apart from producing guilt feelings about 'not pulling their weight', they are not looking at what is causing the extra work in the first place.

Working too long a time, without adequate rest or change is likely to cause errors to increase, which will lead to becoming more inefficient and thus more frustrated, generating more work and, consequently, more stress.

Lastly, overwork can be a way of masking other problems. Overwork can be caused by attempting to get through time missed through a recent traumatic incident, being generally inefficient or not having the necessary competence or skills to do the job. Family problems may encourage a person to stay at work long after colleagues have left – it might be seen as a solution to going home and facing the problem. Either way, dealing with these problems will stop the need for overwork – if it is overwork which has been labelled as a problem. One way or another, overwork will not deal with the real issue.

The following checklist provides some remedies for stress relief.

Detachment

Stand back and take an unemotional look at your work pattern. Is there repetition, interruption or lots of routine change? How much change is present during peaks and troughs?

Organising the day

Be aware of priorities, necessities, everyday routine tasks and occasional work. Try not to duplicate tasks.

Try to understand why

Pretend to be a stranger looking at yourself from a distance. Recognise faults and pressures caused by outside influences.

Diet

Examine your food intake. Try to eat more balanced meals. Never start the day without some nourishment. You are using extra energy without replacement which causes more tension. Remember the inclusion of endorphins and serotonin into your diet.

Calm your nerves

Look at your body as though it were a car battery. If it is not charged up at regular intervals, it will run down and eventually stop. Appreciate the need for relaxation. Even five minutes away from your work station (or home commitments) can lessen the tension. Therefore, have some vital breaks and try practising deep breathing exercises.

Build in helpful rituals like taking a bath. Treat yourself to some self-indulgence, e.g. candles, scent fragrances in the water, music and so on before bed, so that you have unwound and sleep can come. Also be careful what you watch on television, especially if you have been involved in a traumatic incident. Violent or even noisy programmes can trigger off memories of the past trauma, making sleep difficult or flashbacks to appear.

Coping with Stress

1. Develop Problem Solving Skills

- Can you locate precisely the causes of your stress?
- Alternative solutions can be weighed up.
- The right solution can then be selected.

2. Increase Self-Awareness

- How well do you know yourself, your strengths and weaknesses?
- Are you aware exactly how they affect you?

3. Identify and Develop a Support System

- Everyone needs help – can you locate potential sources of support?
- The strongest support may come from family, friends or colleagues.
- Develop a group to share feelings and experiences.
- Learn to communicate more openly.

4. Develop Specific Managerial Skills

- How well can you determine priorities?
- How effectively do you manage time?
- Can you delegate appropriately?

5. Develop Assertiveness Skills

- Can you say 'NO'?
- Using assertiveness techniques, tackle any personality conflicts with your immediate family, friends or colleagues first. You will then be more confident and assertive with authority figures too.

- Remember, people cannot change their behaviour until they are aware of it.

6. Practise Relaxation

- Find a relaxation technique which suits you.
- Make it your own – use it daily to reduce stress.

7. Take Time Out

- Go on a short course or, if very stressed, take a little time off. Just being in a different environment may be all that is needed to re-charge your batteries.

8. Carry out a Job / Life Review

- Develop/widen your professional/personal role to remove frustration.
- Build up outside interests if they seem lacking.

If you find this difficult at this juncture, don't give up as, after a traumatic incident, concentration levels deteriorate. This is quite usual. You may find it difficult to sit down in one place. Read a chapter in a book, but you may find that you repeat the same paragraph time and time again and seem unable to retain the information you have read. This is quite usual – your concentration will come back at some stage as you process the trauma.

Balancing Psychological Stress

As awareness grows, individuals will be more able to identify the stresses that affect them and to decide whether their stress response to each situation has a constructive or destructive effect.

Having recognised their own stress response, they will be better equipped to adopt a more positive approach and, as stress management skills are developed and practised, the risk of long term associated health problems can be reduced.

The Way Forward

Stress must be seen as part of everyone's agenda – whether it be on a personal, psychological or business level. We cannot ignore it! If an individual is to adopt a positive approach and look at stress in a constructive way, positive action is required.

11

Trauma and its Effects on the Family

The effect on the immediate family may be quite dysfunctional in its impact. Dealing with the traumatised member of the family can be like walking on egg-shells. For instance, the survivor can be irritable and this can be displayed by taking it out on members of the family. The children may be demanding or noisy and the survivor may soon lose his or her sense of being rational and could find it difficult, if not impossible to keep calm.

Sex can be a problem for the partner of the survivor, who may be either demanding and aggressive, so that lovemaking becomes more about self-satisfaction than a joyful, fun making, loving/caring experience. On the other hand, there may also be a possibility that the survivor might begin to suffer from impotence. This could be in loss of desire in the female, or a difficulty in maintaining an erection in the male, due to reactive depression caused by the after-effects of the trauma. Naturally this can be disturbing and bring about unhelpful dynamics in the family. The partner can feel rejected or used according to the symptoms being displayed. Within the immediate family dynamic, this may lead to irritability and frustration.

The trauma may be picked up by the rest of the family members, which is known as 'cross fertilisation'. This can be difficult to treat for a number of reasons:-

A. The therapist usually only sees the survivor.

B. The condition is reported to the therapist as irritability or bad behaviour by another member of the family.

C. Family issues may not be asked about by the therapist if doing a short-term, focused therapy.

Some reactions that can be given by the family which may be of assistance:

- Love him or her and make the person welcome.
- Listen to what he or she may say.
- Face the reality of what has happened – don't ignore it.
- Commend efforts and success and try to ignore the slips.
- Trust him or her as an essentially normal, upstanding, competent person.
- Expect the person to be different in some ways.
- Allow time and freedom in getting acquainted with old places and re-establishing old contacts.
- Create an atmosphere of expectancy: encourage him or her to take up a favourite hobby or sport, to go back to work as soon as able, and to lead a normal social life – but avoid pushing or regulating (like the military).
- Get professional help if it is needed. Don't just muddle through.
- Let your own faith and beauty of spirit be your chief stock in trade.

It is important to note that the survivor has had a severe shock to the system. If the survivor had been involved in an accident crossing the road and had been knocked down and suffered a broken arm, it would be in plaster and in a sling. The individual would take great care of it. The trauma that has been suffered cannot be seen, but nevertheless it is as severe. Therefore the survivor needs rest, a little self-indulgence and, most of all, being taken care of. The culture we live in expects that we be stoical and get back to work as soon as possible – this is not realistic or fair.

Listen to the demands of the body and do things at the appropriate time – this will pay dividends.

12

Dealing with the Recurrent Effects of Trauma due to Court Appearances

There is a difficult clinical decision that constantly needs to be made after a road traffic accident (RTA) or after a raid on a bank or shop. This relates to the additional trauma the client may suffer after the initial impact of the incident when he or she learns that litigation, leading to a subsequent court hearing, is likely to take place.

The difficulty which will then present will be the reawakening of the trauma by the court and/or the thought of a court appearance which may be weeks or even months in the future.

All the good therapeutic work which has been carried out by the clinician may then disappear at the thought of the impending hearing or the court case, as undoubtedly old scenarios and places are revisited. Unfortunately, although they have to carry out their work, court officials often become insensitive to the traumatic stress-reawakening reactions their questions will produce. This often appears to the clinician who may be present during the court hearing that all the previous hard work with the client may have to start again and further counselling interventions will be required in order to allow the client to gain the necessary support.

The psychological debriefing will have been carried out within approximately one week after the incident and, if on assessment, more help is required, then further support counselling will have been provided. It is at this stage, or even sooner, that decisions about a possible court case will make itself known. This will cause the client to develop negative, worrying thoughts which then prevent any further improvements being made during sessions addressing the initial trauma. How can this obstacle be overcome?

By re-examining the original Impact of Events Scale (IES – see appendix 4), it might be seen that the client has slipped back to the original reading of the scale, which could confirm that the client is suffering from an acute reaction. It could also become evident that since there is now a considerable gap between the first impact and the court hearing, the client is showing symptoms of the more serious condition of PTSD (Post Traumatic Stress Disorder). Whatever the diagnosis, a re-run of what has taken place in court can sometimes be helpful during a second debriefing. This allows the client to re-tell the experience which should provide some therapeutic value. A recent comment made by a judge during a hearing about a fatal road traffic accident was that the punishment could be therapeutic. What the judge did not appreciate was that the actual punishment, in this case a prison sentence, was the least of the problem. The main criterion is learning to live with and cope with the guilt the client will feel – and how to forgive oneself.

In the majority of instances, court appearances will concern individuals with being called as a witnesses to a crime. Having to identify the intruder/raider/robber or any other offender and possibly having to live with the fear that they may be known to or be recognised by the offender is, in itself, a daunting experience. The effects of these thoughts can be paralysing, causing severe hyper-vigilance (awareness of people and surroundings and the person's own whereabouts). This alone can cause physical symptoms such as palpitations, acute anxiety, panic attacks, severe headache on arrival at the work-place, nausea, vomiting and possible diarrhoea. Sleepless or disturbed nights might be another symptom for no apparent reason. In other words, one is not reliving the event in one's mind – it appears more as a restlessness. It may seem in some ways that dissociation is taking place, but it is more as if the unconscious mind has caused the restlessness in its bid to eliminate the uncomfortable and hurtful memories.

There are numerous ways for the clinician to work with the client according to their preferred working model and the individual suitability for each client. Not every model will be suitable for every client and it will be dependent upon skill, training and experience of the clinician to assess which model will be of most benefit to the client. It would be correct to say that an intervention that stays with the client at their point of distress and uncomfortableness is the place for the clinician to proceed from.

One would hope to move on from this point carefully in the client's own time to a process of desensitisation for the uncomfortable memory, at the same time building places of safety into the structure. This is a secure space in the mind of the client to retreat to if the recalled material has an unsafe or frightening effect. After a moment or two of repose, the client is carefully moved back into the uncomfortable zone of recall until the anxiety levels return to tolerance levels.

EMDR (Eye Movement Desensitisation Reprocessing) is another method which, at this point can produce positive results. Clients are never taken beyond their endurance level. They are always given a choice to retreat to a place of safety but at the same time encouraged to move forward.

It is important for clients to know that they are revisiting this disturbing area with the help and presence of a clinician. It is also essential for them to hear from and to be reassured by the clinician that they have survived the immediate impact. This next stage can be seen as a re-visiting in the knowledge that they are now safe.

Although court appearances upset the supportive treatment of trauma, it may be true to consider that perhaps the ups and downs of the experiences from incident to court case can in some way be beneficial to the client, in that the process is prolonged. The material is therefore dealt with in more detail over a longer period of time. However, the suffering and anxiety that a pending court case can cause may also upset the clinician adversely.

Finally, a client who has a court case pending needs adequate support not only from the clinician but from management and work colleagues. It is almost another trauma to endure, to be placed in a witness box and re-call the event, for whatever reason. The effect of this is not only physically draining but mentally as well. To be able to acknowledge and empathise with the client can make the load a little more endurable. The effect of being told to pull oneself together is damaging and, in most cases impossible since it will be a case of mind over matter and, in cases of trauma, the mind plays a very strong and unmanageable part without professional support.

13

Prevention is better than cure

Industrial and commercial outlets are dependent on regular and effective output of products as well as a workforce which is properly trained, has all the necessary tools available and benefits from a safe working environment.

Although the majority of managers make sure that the company works on oiled wheels by providing supervision and staff who can deal with employee problems when they occur, it is often difficult to identify the cause when a member (or members) of the work force shows signs of slowing down, unusual behaviour not normally found and even reporting sick more frequently than usual.

In some cases it is very difficult to identify the presence of post traumatic stress reactions, particularly if an incident has happened outside the workplace. Management often believe that they are not responsible for anything which occurs outside the gates of the workplace. What they fail to understand is that unless the member of staff has a medical problem which requires treatment and possible subsequent time off work, they are unlikely to talk about any incident which may have happened outside working hours. However, this does not prevent them from having what to them are abnormal reactions which cannot be explained away easily. These reactions will sooner or later have adverse consequences and the job will suffer.

Many working hours may be lost through lack of recognition that a problem exists which, without some form of intervention, will continue to prevent the individual from achieving top performance in the job.

It frequently comes to light through gentle probing that family relationships are under pressure which then have an adverse effect on job performance. This could cause dangerously low concentration levels where the safety of others is put at risk. For example, in multi-tasking work where concentration levels have to be at the highest peak, thoughts about family issues which tend to invade the mind can cause serious lapse of concentration.

Research has shown that reduction of anxiety levels can be achieved by providing the workforce with information-based workshops to prepare for any incidents which might produce trauma. Should an incident happen in the workplace which not only involves people in the immediate vicinity but also colleagues and others who learn about the incident by word of mouth, the reactions could be far worse if the workforce are not prepared for such eventualities. It may well take some considerable time for professional help to take over and deal with crisis intervention.

At this point, any traumatised person will be unable to make decisions, or put into perspective what has just occurred. Since it is vital to provide quick, practical support for those affected, the organisation would benefit greatly by appointing suitable support staff, chosen from the workforce and trained by professionals. This support staff will be able to act as a 'prop' and prevent the traumatised individual from slipping into a more stressful state.

Trauma Support Groups

A trauma support group is an organised group meeting, run by two qualified trauma specialists, which is held for the benefit of those who may have found themselves at the receiving end of a traumatic experience.

The aim is to provide understanding, support and guidance. It will also help establish a coping mechanism with the reactions of post traumatic stress and the more far reaching responses of post traumatic stress disorder (PTSD).

If, after an incident, a group of employees are showing signs of traumatic stress reaction and require further support after debriefing, such a group can easily be set up within the organisation. Groups can accommodate up to ten participants, they run for ten sessions once a week and each meeting lasts for one and a half hours. There are always two qualified people in attendance who are experienced in running such groups.

Aspects of confidentiality are discussed during the meetings and agreed by the group at the outset. If necessary, permission may be asked to discuss an individual's case with a GP but this would only be done with that person's full knowledge and consent.

Members of the community not on a workforce payroll and therefore not able to benefit from such organised care, who have been involved in an incident which might induce traumatic stress reactions or who find themselves recalling past traumatic experiences should not try and bottle it up and hope that it will go away again.

They must make the decision to find support, by seeing their GP who will steer them in the right direction. Doctors are aware of the various forms of help which are available and will refer clients to the most suitable service.

14

The Dynamic of Trauma

A disaster can have the effect of bringing people together in a common cause. If one cares to read the history books, one would soon see that traumatic incidents such as seen in World War II brought people together. They were bound by their experiences of suffering and loss and it appears that it is at this time that human nature usually responds in a good, positive way in generally looking out for each other.

In the London bombings of World War II (as in any other major city), people shared horrific experiences in a common place, together, in air raid shelters, underground stations, and basements and so on, in many different ways. But the accounts, if one takes time to listen to people who were there, is usually the same – they say people were friendly, gave hospitality to those whose homes where bombed out, gave generous gifts of food, clothes and items to make life more bearable as well as comradeship, friendship and in some instances courage.

Living in today's society in large cities, we are not usually aware of such generous relationships from relative strangers. People haven't got time, can't be bothered, have their own independent lives to lead. It is rather sad that it needs a traumatic incident for us to share kindred spirits.

There is yet another dynamic in the suffering, pain and experience of trauma, and that is for those who are there, in the thick of it. These people are bound together almost exclusively by the event, so much so, that in the workplace, it can isolate and separate those who were there, against those who were not. So great and powerful is this dynamic it can cause severe relationship problems, and exclusion of the rest of the workforce, with the loss for those who are suffering, if not handled wisely. The rest of the workforce who may not have been affected have such a lot to offer in genuine human kindness and compassion, that if not rigorously worked at, could lead to exclusion for those who are hurting.

Trauma also leaves in its wake a feeling of apathy and severe lethargy. 'What is the use?' 'Why me?' 'Why now?' ‘What is the reason for all this loss?' – large philosophical questions that cannot adequately be answered, but have lasting repercussions according to one’s own life-fulfilling prophecy. If for instance one is an optimist, one will try in one's own time to make some positive interpretation and understanding of these questions. But, on the other hand, if one is a pessimist, then the whole area of questions can propel one on a slippery path to despair and depression. Perhaps the answer to the question we asked in the introduction to the book about 'why are some people affected by trauma and others aren't?' may be partially found in this area of personality.

There is yet another area where the dynamics of trauma affect not only the people involved or in the workforce, but also in the community or wider family. Trauma is like ripples in a pond, it affects the whole, radiating from the centre (impact) out to the periphery. When the aircraft was blown out of the sky at Lockerbie, it was not just the families that were affected nor the community, but rescue workers, telephonists, secretaries that maintained identification lists, news readers, our nation at large, the American nation and so on.

Trauma is difficult to contain. When Michael Burke, the news reader on television, gave his report on Rwanda, with pictures beamed in by satellite across a vast continent, he never realised the effect it would have on the heart of the nation when they gave their donations to help combat the suffering. With instant communications, the reaches of trauma are unlimited and it can affect all of us in the comfort of our homes.

Finally, there is one more dynamic which can be affected and that is in the area of our 'spirituality'. Trauma can dampen our awareness of that which is beyond us, that which we strive for, that which connects us to fellow man and beyond. It can bring a cynicism into our thinking, where we begin to question basic beliefs and values, and it can cause us to almost change our personality, in that we become nearly the opposite. Family and friends can look on in sheer disbelief and anxiety at the decisions and prejudices that come to light. It is almost as if we have gone back to a child-like state where we behave in a child-like way, throwing tantrums, being aggressive and showing no tolerance to other people's arguments. One could, in fact, be tempted to do something that was totally against one's principles like rob a bank or cause a fracas. One shows no sense of shame or guilt – the trauma has eaten our conscience which governs right and wrong. Naturally this is in extreme cases, but the fact is that it can bring up rigorous, deep, spiritual questions which can be difficult to answer. The strongest medicine one can have is to forgive oneself. Tormenting oneself or going on a guilt trip does not help, but being able to hear and realise that we are a victim in a scenario that has shaken up one's 'known world' to the core can be helpful.

The immediate aftermath of a serious trauma is not the time for discussion of people's beliefs and one needs to be aware of making assertions which may cause more distress.

Trauma and death challenge our understanding of God or humanity, the universe and our relationship to Him or it. It will be difficult to concentrate on what is being said by the survivor or members of a group if we have not thought our own way through the issues which arise.

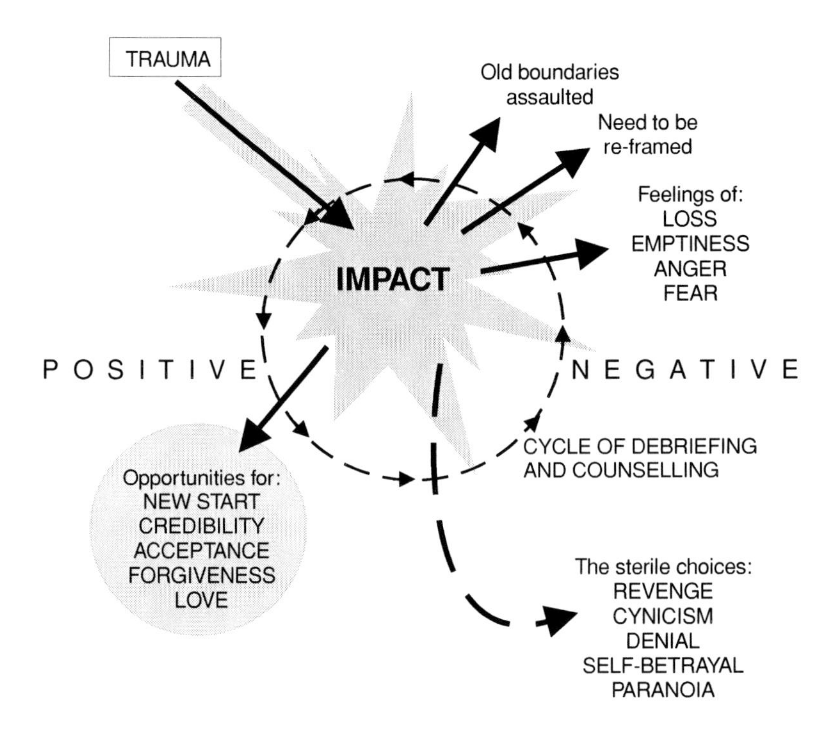

Figure 11 - The negativities of trauma changed through debriefing and counselling to positives

Appendices

Appendix I

DSM-IV

Post Traumatic Stress Disorder

As has already been explained, without fast intervention in the form of psychological debriefing, it is quite likely that the individual could develop the more deep-seated and debilitating condition called post traumatic stress disorder. It would, however be inadvisable to assume that this will be the next development without carrying out an assessment based on the DSM-IV which in this book has been adapted from the *Diagnostic and Statistical Manual of Mental Disorders (4th Edition)*, American Psychiatric Association, Washington DC.

Diagnostic Criteria

A The person has experienced an event that is outside the range of usual human experience and which would be markedly distressing to almost anyone, e.g. a serious threat to one's life or physical integrity, serious threat or harm to one's children, partner or other close relatives and friends, sudden destruction of one's home or community or seeing another person who has recently been, or is being seriously injured or killed as the result of an accident or physical violence.

B The traumatic event is **PERSISTENTLY RE-EXPERIENCED** in at least one of the following ways:

- recurrent and intrusive distressing recollections of the event
- recurrent distressing dreams of the event
- sudden acting or feeling of recurring traumatic events (flashbacks)
- intense psychological distress at exposure to events (i.e. resemblance to the trauma, such as anniversaries).

C PERSISTENT AVOIDANCE of stimuli associated with the trauma or numbing of general responsiveness (not present before the trauma) as indicated by at least three of the following:

- efforts to avoid thoughts or feelings associated with the trauma
- efforts to avoid activities or situations that rouse recollections of the event
- inability to recall an important aspect of the trauma
- markedly diminished interest in significant activities
- feeling of detachment or estrangement from others
- restricted range of feelings, e.g. being unable to have loving feelings
- sense of foreshortened future with negative expectations.

D PERSISTENT SYMPTOMS OF INCREASED AROUSAL (not present before the trauma) as indicated by two of the following:

- difficulty in falling or staying asleep
- irritability or outbursts of anger
- difficulty in concentrating
- hyper-vigilance
- exaggerated startle response

- physiological reactivity upon exposure to events that symbolise or resemble an aspect of the traumatic event (e.g. a woman raped in a lift sweats profusely when entering any lift)

E **DURATION OF SYMPTOMS IN B,C & D** above of at least one month.

DELAYED ONSET is specified if the symptoms start more than six months after the trauma.

Appendix II

GLOSSARY OF TERMS

ABNORMAL:	deviation from the 'norm'
ASSESSMENT:	an instrument to gauge the level of trauma in: behaviour, cognition, emotion and physical reaction
AVOIDANCE:	the inability or unwillingness to recall a traumatic memory
COGNITION:	thinking process
CRITICAL INCIDENT:	traumatic event
COUNSELLING:	giving traumatised individuals the opportunity to make their own decisions and choices by examining options and moving forward
CRISIS INTERVENTION:	the offering of practical support to survivors at the point of impact immediately after a traumatic incident
DEBRIEFING:	a process of retelling a traumatic incident which allows the survivors to work through the event in a structured way, and make sense of what has happened
DYNAMICS:	force of change, either covert or overt – negative (chaos/confusion) or positive (communication/healing)
FLASHBACKS:	recurring images, sounds, smells, taste and touch associated with an original traumatic incident
NEGATION:	denial - refusal to accept an unpleasant situation

PSYCHOSOMATIC: psychological and physiological aspects of all normal and abnormal bodily reactions

POST TRAUMATIC STRESS DISORDER: a chronic/acute development after a traumatic incident which has been allowed to develop without possible intervention

PSYCHOLOGICAL TESTS: a means of measuring the level of disturbance after a traumatic incident

REACTION: the body's normal coping mechanism to shut out and deal with a traumatic shock

RE-ENTRY: the opportunity to return to the 'here and now' after the debriefing process which is the final stage of the process

STRESS: the body's reaction to an event, influence or circumstance which is beyond an individual's ability to cope

TRAUMA: a happening outside the normal range of events which causes physical/emotional shock

TRAUMA SYMPTOMS: a sign or reaction to past trauma, either physical, emotional, behavioural or cognitive

TRIGGER: a stimulus to any of the senses which brings into conscious level a past traumatic incident

Appendix III

HAD Scale

Name:	Date:

Tick only one box in each section

I feel tense or wound-up

- most of the time ☐
- a lot of the time ☐
- time-to time, occasionally ☐
- not at all ☐

I still enjoy the things I used to enjoy

- definitely as much ☐
- not quite as much ☐
- only a little ☐
- hardly at all ☐

I feel as if I am slowed down

- nearly all of the time ☐
- very often ☐
- sometimes ☐
- not at all ☐

I get sort of frightened - feeling like butterflies in the stomach

- not at all ☐
- occasionally ☐
- quite often ☐
- very often ☐

Appendix IV

Impact of Events Scale

Please check each item in the list of comments below and indicate how frequently these comments were true for you ***SINCE THE EVENT****. If they have not occurred, please mark the 'not at all' column.*

		Not at all	A little bit	Moderately	Quite a bit	Extremely
1	Any reminder brought back feelings about it	**0**	**1**	**2**	**3**	**4**
2	I had trouble staying asleep	**0**	**1**	**2**	**3**	**4**
3	Other things kept making me think about it	**0**	**1**	**2**	**3**	**4**
4	I felt irritable and angry	**0**	**1**	**2**	**3**	**4**

Appendix V

Post Traumatic Growth Inventory

Indicate for each statement below the degree to which this change occurred in your life as a result of your crisis, using the following scale.

1	I did not experience this change as a result of my crisis		
2	I experienced this change to a	**VERY SMALL DEGREE**	as a result of my crisis
3	I experienced this change to a	**SMALL DEGREE**	as a result of my crisis
4	I experienced this change to a	**MODERATE DEGREE**	as a result of my crisis
5	I experienced this change to a	**GREAT DEGREE**	as a result of my crisis
6	I experienced this change to a	**VERY GREAT DEGREE**	as a result of my crisis

A My priorities about what is important in life

B I'm more likely to try to change things which need changing

C An appreciation for the value of my life

D A feeling of self-reliance

Appendix VI

Barnett and Roman Inventory for Trauma (BRIT) Assessment Questionnaire

CRISIS INTERVENTION 0-72 hours	DEBRIEFING Post Traumatic Stress Reactions	SUPPORT COUNSELLING 6 weeks

Scale from 1-5 where 1 is little disturbance and 5 is the highest disturbance. Please ring appropriate score.						SYMPTOMS such as -
1. Have you noted any new physical symptoms?	1	2	3	4	5	Migraine; unable to sleep or get up in the morning; feeling sick or vomiting; physically drained; palpitations; shaky, cold, clammy, sweating; jumpy; numb; headaches ....
2. Do you have any recurring thoughts?	1	2	3	4	5	Intrusive thoughts and ideas; thoughts racing around your mind; or thoughts in slow motion that you cannot get rid of ....
3. Are your emotions less easy to control?	1	2	3	4	5	Crying; temper; sulks; irritable; withdrawn; sad; melancholy, depressed; suicidal ....
4. Are you finding it more difficult to cope?	1	2	3	4	5	Memory; concentration; mood swings; fidgety (cannot keep still); unable to finish reading an article ....
5						

This questionnaire is devised to help members of the medical profession make a quick decision on how to refer or treat their patient. It comes with a complete guide and record card.

Appendix VII

Pathway of Care for Post Traumatic Stress

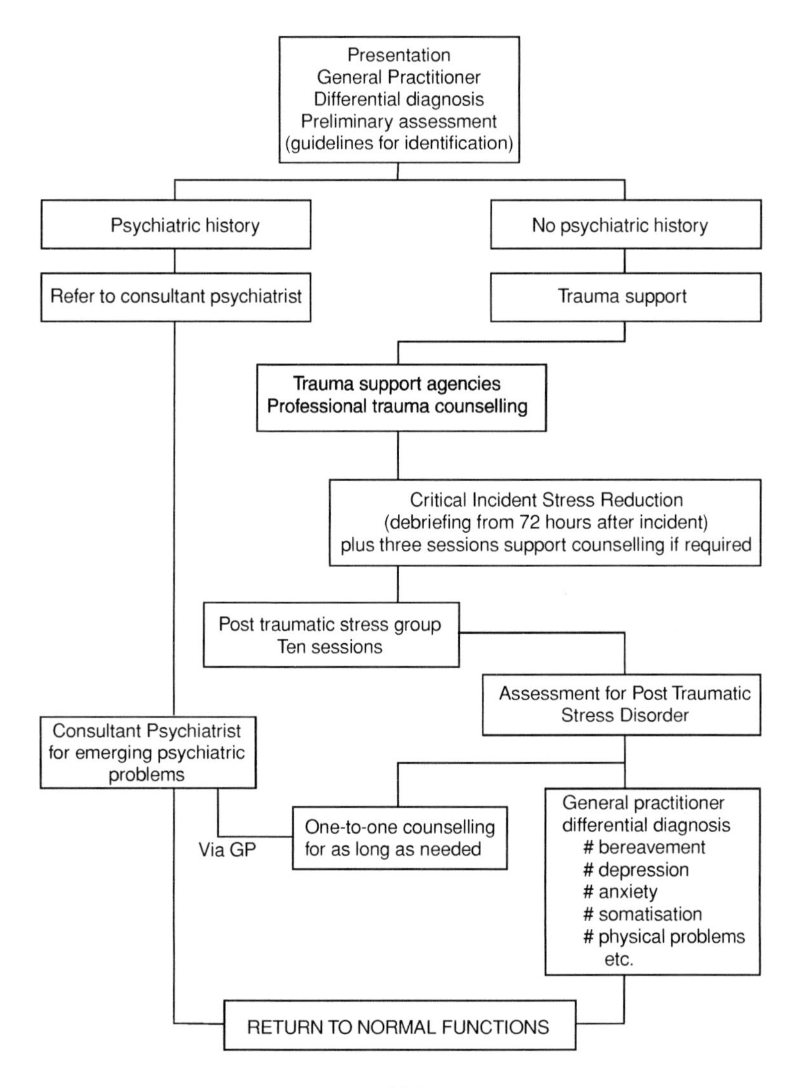

Index

WITHDRAWN